SONGS

CONTENTS

IRISH SONGS
OF RESISTANCE

by

Patrick Galvin

Published by
The Folklore Press
509 Fifth Avenue
New York City

Printed in England

AUTHOR'S NOTE

Thanks are due to Stella Jackson Galvin, whose collaboration at every stage has been invaluable and indispensable.

P.G.

Printed by KENION PRESS LTD., 216 High Street, Slough, Bucks.

I

INTRODUCTION

THE IRISH ARE FAMED AS A NATION OF SINGERS: NOT CHORAL
singers like the Welsh, but soloists—for folk-memories are
long, and there was a time when for Irishmen to meet
together, and to attract attention to themselves by singing their
national songs in chorus, was to court imprisonment or death.
For that matter, solo singing, or even whistling, of certain Irish
airs has been a punishable offence within living memory.

It is difficult to use the term 'folk-song' about what the Irish
call 'national ballads'. In England it is only very few of the songs
of the people, surviving from earlier times, that deal with
current events and real people in straightforward narrative form,
nor are there many composed songs that both express the feelings
of a powerful movement and belong to the people in that they
are as familiar as household words. The vast bulk of Irish songs,
however, are either anonymous reports of actual events, or else
epic appeals to nationhood and love of liberty, composed by men
of letters and other public figures, and universally known and
sung all over the country.

Ireland's national songs are doubly unique. For one thing,
the tradition of writing ballads, of selling broadsheets and
singing ballads at the street-corner or in the market place, has
never died out in Ireland; it is still a *living* tradition to this very

day. In addition, the fact that this tradition has been alive con-
tinuously for a score of generations means that Ireland's songs
reflect Ireland's history with a fidelity probably unparalleled in
the world.

The Irish people have kept these songs alive because they
represented and expressed the people's own powerful and
legitimate emotions and desires. At the same time the songs
helped to direct and canalize action in support of those desires.
The songs are an integral part of Irish history.

Since the history of Ireland is largely that of some 800 years
of resistance to invasion, annexation, absorption, settlement,
enclosure, oppression and exploitation by England, Ireland's
songs sound a continual note of resistance, on many levels. They
may be heroic, bitter, savage, sarcastic or naive. Most of them
are to be grouped broadly into the two categories of rallying-cry
and lament; many have both elements. The majority use narrative
or part-narrative technique.

Even Irish love-songs fall largely under the same headings.
Most are laments; some are rallying-cries; some are actually
'code' songs in which a woman's name is understood to personify
the nation; almost all of them teem with social and historical
content, even when they are not directly 'political'.

This chapter deals only with genuine songs of the Irish
people, the songs that the Irish take in with their earliest breaths,
that are the very atmosphere of Irish family and social life, that
can hardly be localized or even dated, the songs that *are* Ireland.
Considerations on semi-Irish or pseudo-Irish songs will be found
in a later chapter.

It is, of course, inevitable that any collection of Irish national
songs must contain many 'anti-English' references. Considering
the bitterness of the historical reality, the songs are, by and
large, surprisingly moderate and level-headed in this respect,
restricting themselves on the whole to references to named
individuals or specific groups, or else to symbolic generalizations
like 'Saxon'. Few show hatred of *all* the English as a nation; the
hatred is for English landlords, English soldiers, English statesmen.
This is justified by the facts, as a later chapter will show.

It is not, of course, the purpose of this booklet in any way to
aggravate bitterness between the English and Irish peoples, whose
full knowledge and understanding of each other can alone solve
the problems created by this long and troubled history. On the

contrary, it is to be hoped that the digest of Irish history, and its illustration in song, here given will do two things; first help the English to appreciate the unbounded courage and devotion of the unnumbered Irish patriot-heroes, and to realize that their noble spirit is not dead, but is seeking its true direction; and secondly, serve to remind the Irish that at the peak points of their struggle, and under the wisest and most brilliant of their leaders, they have always had sympathy and support from the English people, and that, moreover, they themselves have often been foremost in struggles of the English people in England. For example, the Chartist movement was led by Irishmen; it was the International Working Men's Association, in England, that succeeded in achieving the Fenian Amnesty. Such brotherly help between two peoples, both 'rightly struggling to be free', should thrive on greater knowledge and understanding.

II

BALLAD POETRY AND NATIONHOOD

'NATIONAL POETRY IS THE VERY FLOWERING OF THE SOUL, THE greatest evidence of its health, the greatest excellence of its beauty. . . . It is among all mankind and to all time. It shows us magnified, and ennobles our hearts, our intellects and our country and our countrymen—binds us to the land by its condensed and gem-like history, to the future by examples and aspirations. It solaces us in travel, fires us in action, prompts our invention, sheds a grace beyond the power of luxury round our homes, is the recognized envoy of our minds, presents the most dramatic events, the largest characters, the most impressive scenes, and the deepest passions, in the language most familiar to us.' Thomas Davis. (c. 1843).

Although the history of Ireland is almost wholly that of eight centuries of resistance to English colonization, from the early twelfth century onwards, the great bulk of the national ballads (in the English language) date from the nineteenth century, and above all from the mid-nineteenth century, the period of Thomas Davis and *The Nation* (the 1840's) and the Fenian Brotherhood (the 1860's).

Irish resistance in the earlier periods (up to the early eighteenth century) could not be called 'national' in the modern sense. Shakespeare's Irishman, Macmorris (in *Henry V*), says: 'My nation? What is my nation? I have no nation.' This raises a laugh today, but Shakespeare was historically accurate. At the time of the Norman invasions, the Irish social system was still that of the clan-brotherhood. Classic feudalism itself was a foreign importation hotly resisted (the more so since it was the feudal concept of overlordship and vassalage that gave Henry II his legal excuse for invasion after the Irish chieftain MacMurrogh had paid feudal homage to him). Even the feudal concept of national cohesion in a pyramid structure under a central monarch was foreign to the Irish, whose High King had had only very limited and qualified jurisdiction over the independent Kings and chieftains. The rise of nationalism in the modern sense, as part of the break-up of feudalism and the emergence of capitalism, passed Ireland completely by, for economic and political reasons. Economically, because as a colony her role was merely that of producing raw materials, industry and manufacture being prohibited; politically because she was either completely ignored or used simply for plunder and forced recruiting. The period after 1485-1640, which in England was a time of enormous and fertile social ferment, with the modern world at every point breaking through the shackles of the old in dazzling strength and promise and with agonising birthpangs, in Ireland showed nothing very new. A sort of feudalism was more or less stabilized; during the Wars of the Roses Ireland had been left alone under the Geraldines (who were intermarried with the House of York, and were Lords Deputy for three generations); Henry VII victoriously invaded Ireland and enforced new English property laws by barbarous force; the whole period consists of 'clearing and plantation'— that is, the confiscation of Irish-held land—and bitter local fighting. The net result was the Protestant Settlement of the northern counties and the establishment of a permanent garrison. All the Irish resistance was local and still associated with the clan system under the O'Neills, O'Donnells and Fitzgeralds.

The Cromwellian Revolution in England threw Ireland into confusion, with a Protestant Parliamentary faction, a Protestant King's Party, and a Catholic Royalist League. The Cromwellian invasion of Ireland was a political move to buy off the malcontent left-wing of the Parliamentary Army (the Levellers) with promises of plunder (instead of their arrears of pay); when General Monk (a Leveller sympathiser) began negotiations with Owen Roe O'Neill, Cromwell landed in person and ordered the sack of Drogheda. The Irish were punished savagely, both for being Royalist and, paradoxically, for being potential Levellers; to them, however, it appeared merely that the English revolutionaries were the same barbarous tyrants as the English they had known before.

Cromwell gave the surviving Irish fighters the choice of exile or death; the 34,000 who took service with foreign Kings were the first 'Wild Geese'. After the Restoration the Irish received no help from the prudent Charles II, but were involved in the Jacobite struggle when James II was forced to abdicate and flee; hoping for redress of grievances, they invited James to Dublin; Derry and Enniskillen stood siege *against* the Jacobites, Limerick and Galway *for* the Jacobites; William of Orange invaded Ireland (with a non-British army) and was victorious. There followed the second Flight of the Wild Geese and the savage Penal Laws, under which Ireland lay crushed in almost total silence for nearly fifty years.

So far, no concept of nationhood had shown itself. Everything was local and partisan. O'Neills, O'Donnells and Fitzgeralds might or might not join forces. Ireland could be split disastrously between the rival claims to the throne of England of 'a French Scot and a Spanish Dutchman'. The clans were broken and the people 'lower than the beasts of the field'. Ireland was nothing but a source of viciously extorted wealth.

The first voice to rouse the Irish from the absolute apathy and despair into which they had sunk was that of Jonathan Swift, whose scarifying, vitriolic pamphlets *The Drapier's Letters*, and above all that horrifying but explosive polemic *A Modest Proposal*, not only made the English squirm in guilty rage, but kicked the Irish up from the mud into the first dazed and shambling steps towards regained self-respect. Swift's savage whiplash drew blood, and shamed the degraded and the apathetic into the beginnings of action. Within a generation or so, Grattan and

Flood were agitating in the Dublin Parliament for the redress of Irish grievances; the Dungannon Convention achieved mass delegate representation of the whole country; the Volunteers and the Defenders were preparing for insurrection if need be; Wolfe Tone called upon the nation to 'substitute for the denominations of Catholic, Protestant and Dissenter *the common name of Irishman*'. The nation existed, and the nation was boiling over.

Thus Irish nationalism dates from the eighteenth century. The peak point of that century, and the greatest event in Irish history, was the Great Rebellion of 1798. This, in its close association, through its leaders, with the revolutionary movement in France, in its brilliant pre-dating of modern organized political parties in the Society of United Irishmen, in the sharp political thinking of its greatest figure, Theobald Wolfe Tone, and in the absolutely universal support it commanded throughout the whole country, is unique in Irish history and was in fact an abortive revolution rather than yet another defeated insurrection. Its failure was due to a series of natural disasters and unhappy accidents, and to deliberate deception by Napoleon Bonaparte. Its achievements have lived on in the Chartist movement (most of the Charter came from the programme of the United Irishmen), in all closely-organized progressive political parties, and in Tone's declaration that he relied for support not on the gentry but on 'that numerous and respectable class, the men of no property'.

The '98 Rebellion was put down in scenes of barbaric cruelty that sickened even the perpetrators. Except for Emmet's hopeless Dublin insurrection in 1803, there was no further attempt at a general armed rising for fifty years. Irish nationalism became bound up with the political movements for Catholic Emancipation (granted in 1829) and for Repeal of the Act of Union (which is still in force today in Northern Ireland). The Repeal Agitation developed into an agitation for complete independence, in the Young Ireland movement of the 1840's, with which so many of Ireland's most famous names are associated.

The leaders in the 1840's were men whose grandfathers had fought in 1798 and whose fathers had agitated with Daniel O'Connell for Catholic Emancipation. They witnessed the bankruptcy of O'Connell's policy of conciliation and 'moral force' and saw the need for unity of feeling, thought and action. They sensed that the people wanted a focal point around which to rally all their aspirations; and they created a newspaper, *The*

Nation, perhaps the most dynamically effective periodical Western Europe has ever seen.

On the day of its first appearance the newsmen stormed the building in a wild and unappeasable hunger for copies, of which they could not sell enough. The print of 12,000 was sold out in an hour or so, and after a few issues it had over a quarter-of-a-million readers. Its motto was *To create and foster public opinion and make it racy of the soil*. Its founders were Charles Gavan Duffy, John Blake Dillon and Thomas Davis. Its contributors included almost every man and woman of note in Ireland. Its purpose was expressed by Davis in the prospectus: 'Nationality is our great object, a nationality which may embrace Protestant, Catholic and Dissenter . . . the Irishman of a hundred generations and the stranger who is within our gates; not a nationality which would prelude civil war, but which would establish internal independence—a nationality which would be recognized by the world. . . '.

Its publication policy was to use material of any and every type, with no restrictions as to style, manner or personality. Above all, it published innumerable poems, all of which could be and were sung. Outstanding among these are the poems of Thomas Davis himself, which refer to all periods of Irish history and are specifically intended as rallying-cries. To many of the Irish themselves they came as a revelation.

'The songs were sung throughout the land—in the cottage, in the village-forge, in the harvest-field, in the workshop, in the lawyer's chambers, in the students gatherings, at social and political reunions, and in the concert halls—wherever the people assembled. . . . The military authorities complained that soldiers profaned the barracks by singing them. . . . Literary critics at home and in foreign lands admired them, even critics . . . who had no sympathy with the sentiments expressed. *The Times* described the songs as far more dangerous than O'Connell's speeches. They were brought under the notice of the English Parliament. . . . Some of them were read at the "trial" in 1844 of O'Connell and the other Traversers ("the conspirators of Ireland") as being seditious in character. The praise and the censure alike added to their popularity. . . .' (The Young Irelanders, by T. F. O'Sullivan.)

The Young Ireland movement of national unity was shattered by the disaster of the Famine years, 1846 and 1847, when more than one-third of the nation perished—although corn and dairy produce were being exported to England throughout that period. The 1848 insurrection was hardly more than a gesture, fore-doomed to failure. Davis had died in 1845; Meagher, Mitchel and many others were transported; a third of the survivors of the Famine among the common people, encouraged by the English authorities, emigrated to America, many of them dying on the way. Ireland was depopulated; to this day the population is only 4,000,000, as against the estimated 10,000,000 or more before the Famine.

In Ireland there followed a period of peasant resistance to exorbitant rents and other payments, and then the Fenian move-ment, originating with Irish emigrants in America. The Fenians continued *The Nation* tradition (they had a journal of that name) of poems and ballads of the rallying-cry type, but the insurrection of 1867 was confused, ill-timed and mismanaged, and achieved nothing but the creation of more martyrs.

Almost all Irish national songs since the 1840's—that is the great majority of them—are of *The Nation* type. They are com-posed poems (often by well-known writers) containing many allusions to past battles, rebellions, heroes and traitors, intended for singing to traditional airs or popular melodies. *The Nation*, and above all Thomas Davis, caught and fixed the tradition of the genuine aspirations of the common people. It is notable that none of *The Nation* songs are of the wailing type—not even the laments. At their most tragic, they are positive and full of dignity. Nor are they of the narrow and bigoted anti-British type which has since had a vogue in certain circles.

The secret of the success of *The Nation* and its songs lies in the fact that here were splendidly expressed feelings and thoughts that were in actual fact common to the nation as a whole. In a colonized country, the national question and the class question are fused into one, the class exploiter being the same as—or the declared ally of—the foreign invader. It is when the whole people become conscious of this fusion (as in the 1790's or the 1840's) and are themselves welded into a unified opposition to all exploitation as such, that great rebel songs emerge. This remains true even though the songs themselves may deal only with fragmentary aspects of the great struggle. The all-embracing unity of purpose illumines the whole.

III

HISTORY AND SONG ARE ONE

. . . We honour in song and in story
The names of the patriot men . . .

IT IS NECESSARY TO RUN THROUGH THE MAIN PERIODS OF IRISH
history, so that the innumerable references in the songs may
be understood. English people, relying on their own history
books, often tend to feel that the Irish exaggerate the woes of
their country; in fact, one would shrink to set down in cold blood
the full list of the unimaginable and unending brutalities of
reprisal inflicted on the Irish. In almost every generation from
1169 to 1923, their lot was that of murder, torture, eviction,
starvation, forced labour or exile. It says much for the Irish that
their greatest men have always insisted on distinguishing between
the English atrocity-mongers and the good English, whose
support has been welcomed whenever it has been offered; the
wonder is that the Irish remained able to believe in the existence
of the good English at all.

'The Danes'

Ancient Ireland, up to the middle of the twelfth century,
was founded on a system of clan brotherhood, loosely organized
in five Kingdoms (Ulster, Munster, Leinster, Connaught and
Meath), with a High King, whose function was mainly that of
final judge or arbiter in law cases. Ireland became Christian very
early, in the fifth century, without alteration in the Gaelic social
system. Like England, Ireland was subject to periodic raids by
Scandinavian sea-rovers from the eighth century onwards. These
Northern raiders are known collectively as 'the Danes'; they
established a number of seaports (Cork, Dublin, Limerick,
Waterford, Wexford) but no fixed settlements of any importance.
They were ultimately defeated by Brian Boru at Clontarf in 1014,
and driven from Ireland forever.

The Annals of Innisfallen give an account of Brian's address to his forces before Clontarf. He rode through the ranks in the twilight of morning, Good Friday, 23rd April, 1014, accompanied by his son, Morrogh; reminded the troops of the Bloody Sacrifice which was commemorated on that day; and, holding up the Crucifix in his left hand, and his golden-hilted sword in the right, declared he was willing to die in so just and honourable a cause.

Stand ye now for Erin's glory! Stand ye now for Erin's cause!
Long ye've groaned beneath the rigour of the Northmen's savage laws.
What though brothers league against us? What though myriads be the foe!
Victory will be more honoured in the myriads' overthrow.

God of Heaven, bless our banner—nerve our sinews for the strife!
Fight we now for all that's holy—for our altars, land and life—
For red vengeance on the spoiler, whom the blazing temples trace—
For the honour of our maidens, and the glory of our race!

Curses darker than Ben Heder light upon the craven slave
Who prefers the life of traitor to the glory of the grave!
Freedom's guerdon now awaits you, or a destiny of chains—
Trample down the dark oppressor while one spark of life remains!

Men of Erin! men of Erin! grasp the battle-axe and spear!
Chase these Northern wolves before you like a herd of frightened deer.
Burst their ranks, like bolts from Heaven! Down on the heathen crew,
For the glory of the Crucifix, and Erin's glory too!

William Kenealy
(From *King Brian before the Battle*)

Brian and his son both fell at Clontarf, and Rory O'Connor, King of Connaught, became High King, but Diarmuid McMurrogh (the first traitor) did homage to the English King Henry II and thus gave an excuse for the Anglo-Norman invasion.

'The Normans'

While Ireland was still clan-tribal, England was in the phase of ascendant feudalism. Henry II, 'defending the rights of his vassal Diarmuid McMurrogh' (and authorised by the Pope, who was an Englishman, to make himself Lord of Ireland), sent an expedition under 'Strongbow', the Earl of Pembroke, in 1169. Diarmuid was made King of Leinster, married his daughter to Strongbow, and claimed the High Kingship; Strongbow also claimed it, through his wife, after Diarmuid's death in 1171; but Henry II huried to Ireland and exacted homage to himself from

the Kings and Chieftains. Dublin and the area round was
declared forbidden territory ('the Pale') to the Irish, who were
driven off. There ensued three centuries of endless raids and
skirmishings, with a rough division of territory into Norman
plains and valleys and Irish hills and bogs. Many of the Anglo-
Norman settlers, however, became in two generations 'more
Irish than the Irish', and the Statute of Kilkenny, 1367, made it
High Treason to intermarry with the Irish and inflicted savage
land-confiscation penalties on any who adopted Irish names, dress,
customs or speech. In 1394, Richard II attempted to retrieve his
fortunes by an Irish reconquest, but was routed in Wicklow.
Throughout the 'Hundred Years War' and the 'Wars of the
Roses', England ignored Ireland altogether, and there was a
period of relative calm and prosperity.

The Tudors and Stuarts

The period of major transition in England from feudalism to
capitalism, with which the rise of absolute monarchy, the
Protestant Reformation, the Renaissance and so on are associated,
affected Ireland only in so far as the Tudor monarchs imposed
new English property laws on the Irish, and the Stuarts used them
as a possible source of revenue on the one hand and a bargaining
counter on the other. The first Tudor monarch, Henry VII,
found that the long lull had left English rule possible only at the
good will of the Geraldines; he made victorious war on them
(with German and Italian mercenaries), and had six of the
Fitzgeralds hanged together at Tyburn. A long period of 'clearing
and plantation' (that is, eviction and confiscation), with inter-
mittent but very barbarous local fighting, followed. The former
owners could remain as tenants only at exorbitant rents, or the
lands were given to Englishmen dispossessed by enclosures in
England. The whole estates of the O'Neills and the O'Donnells,
covering six counties, were confiscated and 'planted'—this was
the Plantation of Ulster, 1598-1609. A permanent garrison was
created. Irish reprisals were numerous—for example, the poet
Edmund Spenser had to flee for his life (with *The Faery Queen* still
unfinished) before raiders who burnt down the confiscated
house in which he was living. The end of the reign of Elizabeth I
was indeed notable for the complete routing of English expedi-
tions (including that of the Earl of Essex) by the O'Neills and the
O'Donnells, especially Hugh O'Neill and Red Hugh O'Donnell.

O'DONNELL ABOO

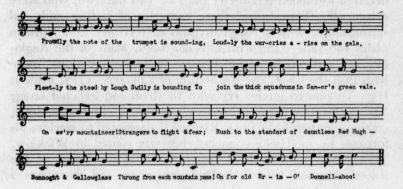

Proudly the note of the trumpet is sounding
Loudly the war-cries arise on the gale,
Fleetly the steed by Lough Swilly is bounding
To join the thick squadrons in Samer's green vale.
    On every mountaineer!
    Strangers to flight and fear;
Rush to the standard of dauntless Red Hugh—
    Bonnoght and Gallowglass
    Throng from each mountain pass!
On for old Erin—O'Donnell—aboo!

Princely O'Neill to our aid is advancing,
With many a chieftain and warrior-clan;
A thousand proud steeds in his vanguard are prancing,
'Neath the borderers brave from the banks of the Bann—
    Many a heart shall quail
    Under the coat of mail;
Deeply the merciless foeman shall rue
    When on his ear shall ring
    Borne on the breeze's wing,
Tirconnell's dread war-cry—O'Donnell—aboo!

Wildly o'er Desmond the war wolf is howling,
Fearless the eagle sweeps over the plain,
The fox in the streets of the city is prowling—
And all who would scare them are banished or slain!
    Grasp, every stalwart hand,
    Hackbut and battle-brand—
Pay them well back the deep debt so long due;
    Norris and Clifford well
    Can of Tirconnell tell—
Onward to glory! O'Donnell—aboo!

Sacred the cause that Clanconnell's defending—
The altars we kneel at, the homes of our sires;
Ruthless the ruin the foe is extending—
Midnight is red with the plunderer's fires!
    On with O'Donnell, then,
    Fight the old fight again;
Sons of Tirconnell all valiant and true!
    Make that false Saxon feel
    Erin's avenging steel!
Strike for your country now—O'Donnell—aboo!

M. J. M'Cann
(Originally entitled *The Clanconnell War Song*)

The rise of Parliamentary revolt in England, and the English Revolution, affected Ireland in that Strafford's repressive rule (aimed at levying money for King Charles I) put several restrictions on Irish manufactures and instituted a regular army. The recall and execution of Strafford in 1641 was the signal for an Irish revolt and a 'displanting' of Ulster by the O'Neills and O'Donnells. Charles's request to Parliament for money to finance reprisals aroused suspicions that the Irish rising was a Royalist trick. The outbreak of civil war in England saw Ireland divided between pro-Parliamentary Dissenters, pro-Charles Protestants, and Catholic Royalists, with considerable inconclusive fighting. Owen Roe O'Neill returned from Spain, repudiated two truce negotiations by the Protestant party, and formed his own army. After Charles's execution, however, he opened negotiations with the Parliamentary General Monk. Parliament ordered Monk to cease negotiations, and Owen Roe O'Neill died soon after, allegedly by poison.

Did they dare, did they dare, to slay Eoghan Ruadh O'Neill?
Yes, they slew with poison him they feared to meet with steel.
May God wither up their hearts! May their blood cease to flow!
May they walk in living death, who poisoned Eoghan Ruadh!

Cromwell landed in person and sacked Drogheda and Wexford; after a solitary victory at Clonmel the Irish surrendered at Kilkenny in 1652. The 34,000 'Wild Geese' chose service with foreign Kings rather than death on the gallows.

How solemn sad by Shannon's flood
The blush of morning sun appears!
To men who gave for us their blood,
Ah! what can women give but tears?

How still the field of battle lies!
No shout upon the breeze has blown!
We heard our dying country's cries,
We sit deserted and alone.
Ogh hone, ogh hone, ogh hone, ogh hone,
Ah! what can women give but tears?

Ireland was destitute, with whole counties depopulated. Massive confiscations and 'transplantings' ('Get to Hell or Connaught') took place; the whole of Ireland was 'landlordised' and a prey to hordes of speculators. Thousands upon thousands of homeless children, orphaned in the fighting, were forcibly slave-transported *en masse* to the West Indies; as they were sold for cash, this was a profitable trade, and was soon supplemented, and then replaced, by wholesale kidnappings, which were officially winked at until finally some English children were kidnapped and the traffic was stopped. (To this day there are West Indian negroes bearing Irish names, which were taken long ago from their masters, who were descendents of these slave children.)

The Irish received no help from Charles II, but had hopes of the Catholic James II, whom some of them supported after his abdication. James landed in Dublin in 1689 and had to summon a Dublin Parliament to deal with the anti-Jacobite cities of Derry and Enniskillen. This 'Patriot Parliament' seized the opportunity; it declared itself independent of England, revoked the Cromwellian Settlement and threatened to confiscate the property of absentee landlords unless they recognized James as King. This served only to lose James many of his English supporters. William of Orange, now King of England, invaded Ireland in 1690, with a force of Danes, Dutch, French, Prussians and Swedes. He crossed the Boyne and defeated Patrick Sarsfield, who fell back on Limerick.

The situation in the seventeenth century was very confused, and of little real hope for Ireland; songs about this period may support either side. The famed *Lilliburlero* 'whistled James from his throne'; *The Royal Blackbird* is Jacobite; *The Battle Of The Boyne* is Williamite; and so on. Here is part of the most popular version of the last-named.

THE BATTLE OF THE BOYNE

July the First in Oldbridge town,
There was a grievous battle,
Where many a man lay on the ground,
By the cannons that did rattle.

> King James he pitched his tents between
> The lines for to retire;
> But King William threw his bomb-balls in,
> And set them all on fire.
>
> When we the Boyne began to cross,
> The enemy they descended;
> But few of our brave men were lost,
> So stoutly we defended;
> The horse were the first that marched o'er,
> The foot soon followed after;
> But brave Duke Schomberg was no more,
> By venturing over the water.
>
> The Protestants of Drogheda
> Have reason to be thankful,
> That they were not to bondage brought,
> They being but a handful,
> First to the Tholsel they were brought,
> And tied at the Millmount after;
> But brave King William set them free,
> By venturing over the water.

A much older version of this song is *The Boyne Water*. Here are the first and last stanzas.

THE BOYNE WATER

July the First, of a morning clear, one thousand, six hundred and ninety,
King William did his men prepare, of thousands he had thirty;
To fight King James and all his foes, encamped near the Boyne Water,
He little feared, though two to one, their multitudes to scatter.

So praise God, all true Protestants, and I will say no further,
But had the Papists gained the day, there would have been open murder,
Although King James and many more were ne'er that way inclined,
It was not in their power to stop what the rabble they designed.

James fled back to France, Marlborough captured Cork and Kinsale, and in 1691 the Irish Jacobites were utterly routed at Athlone and Aughrim; Galway and Limerick surrendered. The second Wild Geese (10,000) fled abroad. The anniversary of the Battle of Aughrim has become the red letter day of the Orange sectaries of Northern Ireland, where 12th July is to this day an occasion for ostentatious displays of hostility to Irish Republicanism.

Here is the most famous and the most beautiful of the Irish Jacobite songs.

THE ROYAL BLACKBIRD

Upon a fine morning for soft recreation,
I heard a fair damsel making much moan,
Sighing and sobbing with sad lamentation
And saying: My blackbird most royal has flown;
My thoughts they deceive me,
Reflection it grieves me,
And I'm overburdened with sad misery,
But if death should bind me,
As true love inclines me,
I'll seek out my blackbird wherever he be.

The birds of the forest they all flock together
The turtle has chosen to dwell with the dove,
And I am resolved in fair or foul weather
Once more in the springtime to seek out my love;
He is all my heart's treasure,
My joy without measure,
Oh, love me, my love, for my heart is with thee,
He is constant and kind
And courageous of mind,
And I'll seek out my blackbird wherever he be.

But if by the fowler my blackbird is taken
Then weeping and wailing will be all my tune,
But if he's alive, and I'm not mistaken,
I surely will see him in May or in June;
For him through hell-fire,
Though the journey be dire,
I'll go, for I love him to such a degree,
Who is faithful and kind
And so noble of mind
That he carries a blessing wherever he be.

And not the wide ocean can fright me with danger,
For though like a pilgrim I wander forlorn,
I may meet with some friendship from one that's a stranger
Before anyone that in England was born;
Oh, Heaven, so spacious,
To England be gracious,
Though some there be odious to both him and me,
For bay of renown,
And laurel, shall crown,
My blackbird with honour wherever he be.

The battle of Aughrim is commemorated in one of the grimmest of the laments.

AFTER AUGHRIM'S GREAT DISASTER

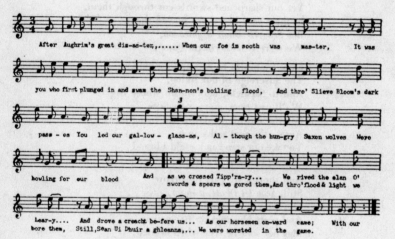

After Aughrim's great diaster,
When our foe in sooth was master,
It was you who first plunged in and swam
The Shannon's boiling flood,
And through Slieve Bloom's dark passes
You led our gallowglasses,
Although the hungry Saxon wolves
Were howling for our blood.

And as we crossed Tipp'rary
We rived the clan O'Leary,
And drove a *creacht* before us
As our horsemen onward came;

With our swords and spears we gored them
And through flood and light we bore them,
Still, *Sean Ui Dhuir a ghleanna*,
We were worsted in the game.

Long, long we kept the hillside,
Our couch hard by the rillside,
The sturdy knotted oaken boughs
Our curtain overhead;
The summer's blaze we laughed at,
The winter's snows we scoffed at,
And trusted in our long steel swords
To win us daily bread.

Till the Dutchman's troops came round us,
In fire and steel they bound us,
They blazed the woods and mountains
Till the very clouds were flame,
Yet out sharpened swords cut through them,
In their very hearts we hewed them,
But *Sean Ui Dhuir a ghleanna*,
We were worsted in the game.

Here's a health to *your* and *my* king,
The Sovereign of our liking,
And to Sarsfield, underneath whose flag
We'll cast once more a chance;
For the morning's dawn will bring us
Across the seas and sing us
To take our stand and wield a brand
Among the sons of France.

And though we part in sorrow,
Still, *Sean Ui Dhuir, a chara*,
Our prayer is—God Save Ireland
And pour blessings on her name;
May her sons be true when needed,
May they never feel as we did,
For *Sean Ui Dhuir a ghleanna*,
We were worsted in the game.

The Irish Brigades formed at foreign courts by the Wild Geese were the most famed and formidable soldiers of all Europe in their day. Sarsfield lived to make his former victor William of Orange turn tail at the battle of Landen, where Sarsfield died with the words: 'Oh that this were for Ireland!' It was Clare's Dragoons—'each looks as if revenge for all were staked on him alone'—who turned the tide against the English at Fontenoy, and caused George II to exclaim: 'Cursed be the laws which deprive me of such subjects!'.

CLARE'S DRAGOONS

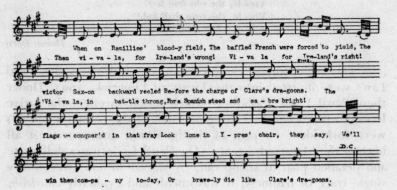

When, on Ramillies' bloody field,
The baffled French were forced to yield,
The victor Saxon backward reeled
Before the charge of Clare's dragoons.
The flags we conquered in that fray,
Look lone in Ypres' choir, they say,
We'll win them company today,
Or bravely die like Clare's dragoons.
    Viva la, for Ireland's wrong!
    Viva la, for Ireland's right!
    Viva la, in battle throng,
    For a Spanish steed and sabre bright!

Another Clare is here to lead,
The worthy son of such a breed;
The French expect some famous deed,
When Clare leads on his bold dragoons.
Our colonel comes from Brian's race,
His wounds are in his breast and face,
The *bearna baoghail* is still his place,
The foremost of his bold dragoons.
    Viva la, the new brigade!
    Viva la, the old one too!
    Viva la, the rose shall fade,
    And the shamrock shine for ever new!

Oh! comrades, think how Ireland pines,
Her exiled lords, her rifled shrines,
Her dearest hope, the ordered lines,
And bursting charge of Clare's dragoons.
Then fling your green flag to the sky,
Be *Limerick*! your battle-cry,
And charge, till blood floats fetlock-high
Around the track of Clare's dragoons.

Viva la, the new brigade!
Viva la, the old one too!
Viva la, the rose shall fade,
And the shamrock shine for ever new!

Thomas Davis

The anti-Catholic clauses known to history as the Penal Laws were inserted into the Treaty of Limerick, 1697. Under these Penal Laws, Catholics (which meant in effect the native Irish of every class, and the great bulk of the common people) were forbidden, on pain of death, almost any activity at all beyond the barest subsistence. The Penal Code was a deliberate and detailed plan to stamp out, by starvation and force, every single trace of Irishness. It was openly and explicitly *anti-Irish*, and made the Irish literally a race of beggars. 'The peasant scarce had leave to live,' wrote Davis.

Forbid to plead,
Forbid to read,
Disarmed, disfranchised, imbecile—
What wonder if our step betrays
The freedman, born in penal days?

In balladry, a curious by-product of the Penal Laws is the quaintly learned flavour of the classical allusions in many songs; these odd scraps of antique learning derive from the 'hedge-schoolmasters', the teachers who were driven out on to the roads with the banning of any education for Catholics, and who taught their ragged pupils in the fields in return for crusts of bread.

The Birth Of Nationhood

Under the Penal Laws, Ireland's existing trade and manufactures were systematically destroyed. For example, no meat could be exported except barrelled salted meat for the British Navy; no wool could be exported except to Britain; and so on. Only the linen trade was encouraged and subsidised, to help Britain counter Dutch and French competition. Anglo-Irish capital could be invested only in Britain. The Chief Secretary and the Viceroy were appointed by the British Cabinet; the Irish Ministers were appointed by the Viceroy. No Catholic could vote, and the 'representatives' in the Dublin Parliament were nominated by local landowners, who sold seats openly. Up to 1780 Irish political affairs were a seething mass of corruption. The bulk of the landlords were absentees or 'graziers' (that is, mere receivers of rent who did not themselves farm), and the mass of the people were peasants below subsistence level. The staple diet of the people had become potatoes and buttermilk, while the garrison towns and England received large quantities of Irish-grown wheat and dairy products.

THE GRAZIER TRIBE

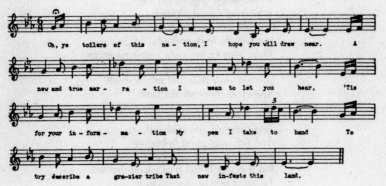

Oh, ye toilers of this nation,
I hope you will draw near.
A new and true narration
I mean to let you hear,
Tis for your information
My pen I take to hand
To try describe a grazier tribe
That now infests this land.

This grazier clan has overran
Your country so fair,
Enough to make the angels weep
Or drive you to despair;
There's not a town from Cork to Down,
Or Dublin to Tralee,
But has a den of grazier men
To keep you in poverty.

Oh, ye men in name have ye no shame
To see this beauteous land,
Turned into one vast wilderness
By a cursed grazier band;
This land so kind was ne'er designed
By providence on high,
To keep John Bull with mutton full
While the natives starve and die.

Oh, ye men of honest labour,
If ever you'd be free,
Now take your stand upon the land
And strike for liberty;
Commit no crime, now is the time,
To burst your galling chains,
And drive this band clean off the land,
As Brian drove the Danes.

So ye valiant sons of labour
Wherever you are found,
To seek a home you need not roam
But quietly look around;
There may be seen fine meadows green,
And bullocks sleek and grand,
Just get your pole and take a stroll
And clear them off the land.

And if Bob be there to fume and swear
And threaten you with jail,
And for your good behaviour
You surely must find bail;
But still you'll find true friends behind
To cheer you in your woe,
Then you'll be so grand with house and land
That yourself you will not know.

In 1727 Swift declared that five-sixths of the nation were
beggars. From about 1730 there were sporadic local riots and a
small patriot opposition in the Dublin Parliament; and in 1761
there was a general peasant rising, the 'Whiteboy Conspiracy' of
active resistance to the enclosure of the common grazing lands.
Loosely connected local secret societies for agrarian self-defence
(later called 'Ribbonmen') were formed, and continued in
existence spasmodically for more than a century. They and other
such societies, Oakboys, Steelmen, Moonlighters, are all lumped
together, with the armed and drilled Volunteers and Defenders,
and the political Society of United Irishmen, and the Catholic
Committee, under the comprehensive generic term 'Croppies'.

The term Croppy has a much-disputed derivation, some
referring it to the cropped ears of convicted felons (any political
action was felony in Ireland), some to the pitch-cap torture
applied to rebels, others to the 'democratic' hair-cut favoured by
the supporters of the French Revolution, others to the fact that
only the lower orders wore their hair short, and others again to
the ancient Gaelic Irish hair-style of a short square-cut bob with a

fringe. The probability is that the term includes all of these connotations, since all of them are factually applicable to the rebel patriot Irish. 'Croppy' is a sort of linguistic cluster, uniting several strands of history in a single word.

There are a great many songs about the Croppies. Some authorities claim that there is a version of *The Croppy Boy* for every county in Ireland. Here is one version.

THE CROPPY BOY

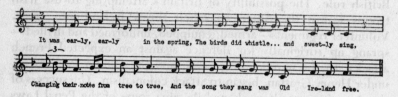

It was early, early in the Spring,
The birds did whistle and sweetly sing,
Changing their notes from tree to tree,
And the song they sang was Old Ireland free.

It was early, early in the night,
The yeoman cavalry gave me a fright;
The yeoman cavalry was my downfall
And I was taken by Lord Cornwall.

'Twas in the guard-house where I was laid
And in a parlour where I was tried;
My sentence passed and my courage low
When to Dungannon I was forced to go.

As I was passing my father's door,
My brother William stood at the door;
My aged father stood at the door,
And my tender mother her hair she tore.

As I was going up Wexford Street,
My own first cousin I chanced to meet;
My own first cousin did me betray,
And for one bare guinea swore my life away.

As I was walking up Wexford Hill
Who could blame me to cry my fill?
I looked behind and I looked before,
But my aged mother I shall ne'er see more.

As I was mounted on the platform high
My aged father was standing by;
My aged father did me deny,
And the name he gave me was the Croppy Boy.

It was in Dungannon this young man died
And in Dungannon his body lies;
And you good people that do pass by
Oh shed a tear for the Croppy Boy.

In 1773 the American colonies suddenly revolted against British rule. The possibility of Britain's attempting to use Irish troops against the American rebels threw Ireland into crisis. Volunteer regiments—armed, equipped, uniformed and drilled—sprang up (originally for defence against an expected French attack), to the number of 50,000, and the Dublin Parliament, under Henry Grattan, began to attack colonialism. The success of the American revolt weakened Britain; some of the Penal Laws were repealed; but the Volunteer movement continued to grow.

From the citizen-soldiers the foe fled aghast—
Still they stood to their guns when the danger was past,
For the voice of America came o'er the wave,
Crying: Woe to the tyrant, and hope to the slave!

In 1782 the Ulster Volunteer Convention (of delegates of all denominations) at Dungannon expressly repudiated English rights to legislate for Ireland.

Hurrah! 'tis done—our freedom's won—
Hurrah! for the Volunteers! . . .
The chain is broke—the Saxon yoke
From off our neck is taken;
Ireland awoke—Dungannon spoke—
With fear was England shaken.

Largely under the influence of the enormous impact on progressive hopes of the French Revolution in 1789, the Society of United Irishmen was founded by Theobald Wolfe Tone in 1791.

The Great Rebellion of 1798 and its aftermath

The most striking thing about the Society of United Irishmen is its freedom from the religious sectarianism that had been the bane of Ireland for two centuries and was, alas, destined to reappear latter. Wolfe Tone, a Dublin Protestant, was asked by the Catholic Committee to be their representative; being a nationwide popular movement, the United men were preponderantly Catholic, yet many of their most honoured names are those of Protestants; the Protestant landowner Bagenal Harvey and the croppy priest Father Murphy led the Wexford rising together.

This broadness of vision came from the sound and clear political principle for which Tone is outstanding. He understood (as have no other Irish leaders save perhaps Thomas Davis, Finton Lalor, Charles Stewart Parnell, and James Connolly) not only the imperative need for absolute unity but also the means to achieve it. His programme was simple, clear and practicable. He rejected all attempts at what today we call 'diversionism', and showed himself not only financially but morally incorruptible, in an age when corruption of every sort was the commonplace of daily life. All honest men were invincibly attracted to him and the principles he stood for, which were firmly founded in objective fact and practical possibility. In an age of greatness and among a nation of unnumbered heroes, he stands supreme. Not without reason do the patriot Irish do pilgrimage year by year to pluck a leaf from his grave.

> And Freedom's flower from his grave starts
> And far its seeds are blown
> To bloom anew in boyish hearts
> That honour Young Wolfe Tone.

The immediate aim of the Society of United Irishmen was Parliamentary Reform, in order, said Tone: 'To subvert the tyranny of our execrable government; to break the connection with England, the never-failing source of all our political evils; and to assert the independence of my country'. No Irishman worthy of the name could disagree with these objects; nor with the means, which Tone announced as being: 'To unite the whole people of Ireland, to abolish the memory of past dissensions, and to substitute the common name of *Irishman* in place of the denominations of Protestant, Catholic and Dissenter'.

The nation flamed with enthusiastic response. Tom Paine's *The Rights Of Man* became 'the Koran of Belfast', in Tone's words, and the United Men's programme was approved by the English and Scottish Jacobin Societies (the supporters of the French

Revolution). Chief points in this programme were: Manhood suffrage; equal electoral districts; no property qualification for members of Parliament; annual Parliaments; payment of members. Does that sound familiar to English readers? It should. It is identical with the famous Five Points of the English Chartist movement, which took them up nearly fifty years later, under the leadership of the Irishmen Feargus O'Connor and Bronterre O'Brien.

The United Irishmen also demanded the abolition of tithes, resistance to rack-renting, and sweeping agrarian reforms. Their paper, *The Northern Star* (also a Chartist re-creation later), the first printed patriot journal in Ireland, showed interest in internal English affairs and warmly greeted the publication of Paine's *Age Of Reason* and Mary Wollstonecraft's *Vindication Of The Rights Of Women*. They corresponded with the Jacobin Society in Paris and the London Corresponding Society, sent a delegation to the British National Convention (1792), and made the Scottish Jacobin, Thomas Muir, an honorary member when he was sentenced to fourteen years transportation. In short, they were in the closest touch with progressive movements in Britain and abroad as well as in Ireland.

The Catholic Convention of 1792 demanded full political and economic equality for Catholics, and forced the Catholic Relief Act of 1793, which removed almost all the Penal Laws. England, however, was now at war with revolutionary France. The Society of United Irishmen, all assemblies of delegates, and all import or manufacture or sale of arms, were banned, and Irishmen were conscripted and press-ganged into the British forces. The peasants took to the hills *en masse* and many conscripted men were forcibly rescued. Many of the United leaders were put on trial (the brilliant lawyer J. P. Curran gaining the acquittal of a number of them). Tone went to America to approach the French Ambassador. The secret oath-bound Orange Society was formed with the aim of disrupting the United movement. Tone left America for France, and persuaded the Directors Carnot and Barras to send an Irish expedition under General Hoche. Had this force landed, there might well have been revolution in Ireland.

At Christmas 1796, Tone was on a French ship in Bantry Bay, held off from landing by a contrary wind.

THE SHAN VAN VOCHT

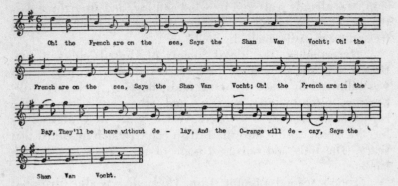

Oh! the French are on the sea, Says the Shan Van Vocht; Oh! the French are on the sea, Says the Shan Van Vocht; Oh! the French are in the Bay, They'll be here without de - lay, And the O-range will de - cay, Says the Shan Van Vocht.

Oh! the French are on the sea,
Says the Shan Van Vocht;
The French are on the sea,
Says the Shan Van Vocht;
Oh! the French are in the Bay,
They'll be here without delay,
And the Orange will decay,
Says the Shan Van Vocht.

And where will they have their camp?
Says the Shan Van Vocht;
Where will they have their camp?
Says the Shan Van Vocht;
On the Curragh of Kildare,
The boys they will be there,
With their pikes in good repair,
Says the Shan Van Vocht.

And what colour will they wear?
Says the Shan Van Vocht;
What colour will they wear?
Says the Shan Van Vocht;
What colour should be seen
Where our fathers' homes have been,
But their own immortal green?
Says the Shan Van Vocht.

And will Ireland then be free?
Says the Shan Van Vocht;
Will Ireland then be free?
Says the Shan Van Vocht;
Yes! Ireland shall be free
From the centre to the sea;
Then hurrah for Liberty!
Says the Shan Van Vocht.

The bulk of the French fleet, however, including Hoche's ship, was already scattered by wind and fog, and after three days the remnant returned to France. Premature local risings in Ireland were easily quelled.

Nevertheless, the illegal Society of United Irishmen continued to grow, in spite of the Insurrection Act of 1797, which was followed by house-to-house raids, flogging, picketing, half-hanging, pitch-capping, roasting and other barbarities as the regular daily round. The overcrowded gaols were cleared by forcible conscription into the British Navy (which mutinied that year). The only and universal hope of the Irish was a French landing.

Tone's second attempt, from Holland, was also frustrated by the wind. His friend Hoche, Bonaparte's rival, died suddenly, perhaps by poison. Bonaparte, now in effect master of France, was playing for time against England, using Ireland as his smokescreen: when the *Armee d'Angleterre* at last sailed in 1798, it was not for Ireland but for Egypt. Tone was left impotently behind in Paris. Civil War broke out in Ireland. The whole of the Leinster leadership of the United Irishmen (except Lord Edward Fitzgerald, who happened to be late) were arrested in a single raid, thanks to the treachery of Thomas Reynolds. German troops were diverted to Ireland from the West Indies. Flogging to death became the order of the day. Edward Fitzgerald's rising was betrayed and he died of his wounds. Each local rising was isolated and all were defeated. Then further risings broke out separately and spontaneously in Antrim (under McCracken), Down, Wexford and Wicklow. Only the Wexford rising had any success; it was remarkable for the dauntless leadership of the 'croppy priests'.

BOULAVOGUE

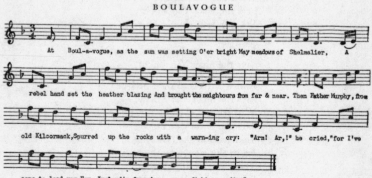

At Boul-a-vogue, as the sun was setting O'er bright May meadows of Shelmalier, A rebel hand set the heather blazing And brought the neighbours from far & near. Then Father Murphy, from old Kilcormack, Spurred up the rocks with a warn-ing cry: "Arm! Ar,!" he cried, "for I've come to lead you, For Ireland's free-dom we fight or die."

At Boulavogue, as the sun was setting
O'er bright May meadows of Shelmalier,
A rebel hand set the heather blazing
And brought the neighbours from far and near.
Then Father Murphy, from old Kilcormack,
Spurred up the rocks with a warning cry;
'Arm! Arm!' he cried, 'for I've come to lead you,
For Ireland's freedom we fight or die'.

He led us on 'gainst the coming soldiers,
The cowardly Yeomen we put to flight;
'Twas at the Harrow the boys of Wexford
Showed Bookey's regiment how men could fight.
Look out for hirelings, King George of England,
Search every kingdom where breathes a slave,
For Father Murphy of the County Wexford
Sweeps o'er the land like a mighty wave.

We took Camolin and Enniscorthy,
And Wexford storming drove out our foes;
'Twas at Slieve Coillte our pikes were reeking
With the crimson stream of the beaten yeos.
At Tubberneering and Ballyellis
Full many a Hessian lay in his gore;
Ah, Father Murphy, had aid come over,
The green flag floated from shore to shore!

At Vinegar Hill, o'er the pleasant Slaney,
Our heroes vainly stood back to back,
And the Yeos at Tullow took Father Murphy
And burned his body upon the rack.
God grant you glory, brave Father Murphy,
And open Heaven to all your men;
The cause that called you may call tomorrow
In another fight for the green again.

                                        P. J. McCall

Final defeat came in June, 1798. Hundreds upon hundreds of captured rebels were publicly hanged and their bodies flung into mass graves or 'croppy holes'. Hundreds more fled the country. In August, 1798, the French General Humbert sailed for Ireland on his own initiative and landed in Mayo. The local peasantry rose *en masse*, but after a great initial victory ('the races of Castlebar'), they were routed and exterminated.

THE MEN OF THE WEST

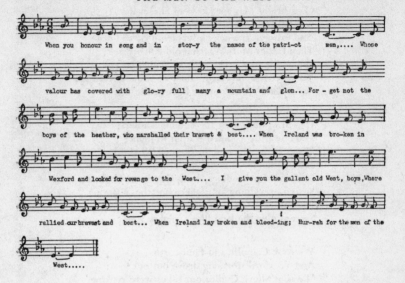

When you honour in song and in story the names of the patriot men, Whose valour has covered with glory full many a mountain and glen... Forget not the boys of the heather, who marshalled their bravest & best.... When Ireland was broken in Wexford and looked for revenge to the West.... I give you the gallant old West, boys, Where rallied our bravest and best... When Ireland lay broken and bleeding; Hurrah for the men of the West.....

When you honour in song and in story the names of the patriot men,
Whose valour has covered with glory full many a mountain and glen,
Forget not the boys of the heather, who marshalled their bravest and best
When Ireland was broken in Wexford and looked for revenge to the West.

> I give you the gallant Old West, boys,
> Where rallied our bravest and best
> When Ireland lay broken and bleeding;
> Hurrah for the men of the West!

The hilltops with glory were glowing, 'twas the eve of a bright harvest day
When the ships we'd been wearily waiting sailed into Killala's broad bay
And over the hill went the slogan, to awaken in every breast
The fire that has never been quenched, boys, among the true hearts of
                                                            the West.

> *Chorus*

Killala was ours ere the midnight, and high over Ballina town
Our banners in triumph were waving before the next sun had gone down.
We gathered to speed the good work, boys, the true men from near and
                                                            afar;
And history can tell how we routed the redcoats through old Castlebar.

> *Chorus*

And pledge me the stout sons of France, boys, bold Humbert and all his
> brave men,
Whose tramp, like the trumpet of battle, brought hope to the drooping
> again.
Since Ireland has caught to her bosom on many a mountain and hill
The gallants who fell, so they're here, boys, to cheer us to victory still.

Chorus

Though all the bright dreamings we cherished went down in disaster
> and woe,
The spirit of old is still with us that never would bend to the foe;
And Connaught is ready whenever the loud rolling tuck of the drum
Rings out to awaken the echoes and tell us the morning has come.

> So here's to the gallant old West, boys,
> Who rallied her bravest and best
> When Ireland was broken and bleeding;
> Hurrah! for the men of the West!

William Rooney

Three weeks later a French force, with Tone (as a Brigadier of the French Army) on the flagship, the *Hoche*, was intercepted in Lough Swilly, and after an epic battle was forced to surrender when the scuppers were knee-deep in blood and the ships were sinking. Tone was taken to Dublin in chains, court-martialled and condemned to death by hanging, but committed suicide in his cell, not knowing that Curran had obtained a writ of Habeas Corpus.

The English at once forced the Act of Union (1800) through the Dublin Parliament, by unparalleled bribery on a gigantic scale, and deprived the Irish of all representation except through Westminster.

Robert Emmet (younger brother of the United Irishman Thomas Addis Emmet), who had seen the bodies of his brother's friends flung into the Croppies Hole, attempted a rising in 1803. His conspiracy was too secret and his preparations too imprecise; it all lasted only a few hours and broke up in confusion. Emmet's whereabouts were betrayed by Curran's 'friend' Leonard McNally; Emmet was arrested and tried—McNally was his defence counsel—and publicly hanged at almost the same time as Tone's best friend, Thomas Russell, who had escaped the '98 reprisals. Ireland relapsed into a temporary apathy of despair.

BOLD ROBERT EMMET

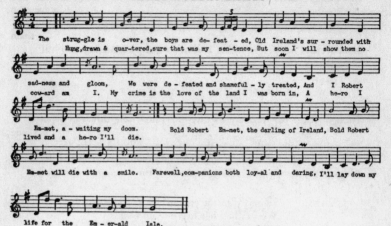

The struggle is over, the boys are defeated,
Old Ireland's surrounded with sadness and gloom,
We were defeated and shamefully treated,
And I, Robert Emmet, awaiting my doom.
Hung, drawn and quartered, sure that was my sentence,
But soon I will show them no coward am I.
My crime is the love of the land I was born in,
A hero I lived and a hero I'll die.

> Bold Robert Emmet, the darling of Ireland,
> Bold Robert Emmet will die with a smile,
> Farewell companions both loyal and daring,
> I'll lay down my life for the Emerald Isle.

The barque lay at anchor awaiting to bring me
Over the billows to the land of the free;
But I must see my sweetheart for I know she will cheer me,
And with her I will sail far over the sea.
But I was arrested and cast into prison,
Tried as a traitor, a rebel, a spy;
But no man can call me a knave or a coward,
A hero I lived and a hero I'll die.

> *Chorus*

Hark! the bell's tolling, I well know its meaning,
My poor heart tells me it is my death knell;
In come the clergy, the warder is leading,
I have no friends here to bid me farewell.
Goodbye, old Ireland, my parents and sweetheart,
Companions in arms to forget you must try;
I am proud of the honour, it was only my duty—
A hero I lived and a hero I'll die.

> *Chorus*

Songs of the '98 Rebellion are 'thick as autumnal leaves', and references to its events and heroes defy calculation: one could insert a song for almost every phrase in the above outline. Here are three more examples.

KELLY THE BOY FROM KILLANNE

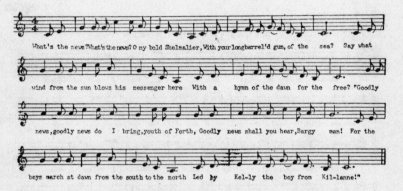

What's the news? What's the news? O my bold Shelmalier,
With your long-barrelled gun, of the sea?
Say what wind from the sun blows his messenger here
With a hymn of the dawn for the free?
'Goodly news, goodly news, do I bring, youth of Forth,
Goodly news shall you hear, Bargy man!
For the boys march at dawn from the south to the north
Led by Kelly the boy from Killanne!'

Tell me who is the giant with the gold curling hair—
He who rides at the head of your band?
Seven feet is his height, with some inches to spare,
And he looks like a king in command!
'Oh, me boys, that's the pride of the bold Shelmaliers,
'Mongst our greatest of heroes, a Man!
Fling your beavers aloft and give three rousing cheers
For John Kelly, the Boy from Killanne!'

Enniscorthy's in flames, and old Wexford is won,
And the Barrow tomorrow we cross.
On a hill o'er the town we have planted a gun
That will batter the gateways to Ross!
All the Forth men and Bargy men march o'er the heath,
With brave Harvey to lead on the van;
But the foremost of all in that grim gap of death
Will be Kelly the Boy from Killanne!

But the gold sun of freedom grew darkened at Ross,
And it set by the Slaney's red waves;
And poor Wexford, stript naked, hung high on a cross,
With her heart pierced by traitors and slaves!
Glory O! Glory O! to her brave sons who died
For the cause of long-down-trodden man!
Glory O! to Mount Leinster's own darling and pride—
Dauntless Kelly, the Boy from Killanne!

P. J. McCall

HENRY JOY MCCRACKEN

It was on the Belfast mountains I heard a maid complain,
And she vexed the sweet June evening with her heart-broken strain
Saying: 'Woe is me, life's anguish is more than I can dree,
Since Henry Joy McCracken died on the gallows tree.

At Donegore he proudly rode and he wore a suit of green
And brave though vain at Antrim his sword flashed lightning keen
And when by spies surrounded his band to Slemish fled
He came unto the Cavehill to rest his weary head.

I watched for him each night long as in our cot he slept;
At daybreak through the heather to MacArt's fort we crept,
When news came from Greencastle of a good ship anchored nigh,
And twas down by yon wee fountain we met to say goodbye.

He says: 'My love be cheerful, for tears and fears are vain'.
He says: 'My love be hopeful, this land will rise again'.
He kissed me ever fondly, he kissed me three times o'er,
Saying: 'Death shall never part us, my love for evermore'.

That night I climbed the Cavehill and watched till morning blazed,
And when its fires had kindled across the loch I gazed;
I saw an English tender at anchor off Garmoyle,
But alas! no good ship bore him away to France's soil.

And twice that night a tramping came from the old shore road;
Twas Ellis and his yeomen, false Niblock with them strode;
My father home returning the doleful story told,
'Alas', he says, 'young Harry Joy for fifty pounds is sold'.

'And is it true?' I asked her. 'Yes it is true', she said,
'For to this heart that loved him I pressed his gory head,
And every night, pale, bleeding, his ghost comes to my side,
My Harry, my dead Harry, comes for his promised bride.'

Now on the Belfast mountains this fair maid's voice is still,
For in a grave they laid her on high Carnmoney hill,
And the sad waves beneath her chant a requiem for the dead:
But the rebel wind shrieks freedom above her weary head.

                           (*Attributed to William Drennan*)

THE RISING OF THE MOON
Air: The Wearing Of The Green

'Oh! then tell me, Sean O'Farrell, tell me why you hurry so?'
'Hush, *a bhuachaill*, hush and listen,' and his cheeks were all aglow.
'I bear orders from the Captain, get you ready quick and soon,
For the pikes must be together at the rising of the moon.'

'Oh! then tell me, Sean O'Farrell, where the gathering is to be?'
'In the old spot by the river, right well known to you and me.
One word more—for signal token—whistle up the marching tune,
With your pike upon your shoulder, by the rising of the moon.'

Out from many a mudwall cabin eyes were watching through the night,
Many a manly breast was throbbing for the blessed warning light,
Murmurs passed along the valley like the banshee's lonely croon,
And a thousand blades were flashing at the rising of the moon.

There beside the singing river that dark mass of men were seen,
Far above the shining weapons hung their own immortal green.
'Death to every foe and traitor! Forward! Strike the marching tune,
And, hurrah, my boys, for freedom! 'tis the rising of the moon.'

Well they fought for poor old Ireland and full bitter was their fate—
Oh! what glorious pride and sorrow fills the name of Ninety-Eight—
Yet, thank God, while hearts are beating in manhood's burning noon
We will follow in their footsteps at the rising of the moon!

                                    John Keegan Casey

From The Act Of Union To Young Ireland

There followed a period of economic and political de-
pression almost as abject as that of a hundred years before.
Ireland presented a picture of unrelieved rackrenting land-
lordism, with emigration as the people's only hope of better-

ment. As the Industrial Revolution progressed in England, Ireland was forced inexorably into the role of supplier of cheap foodstuffs, raw materials, labour and investment capital. The people had no alternative but land-work; and any improvements they made in their equipment or their crops merely increased the rent and tithes. There were cases of rent exceeding the total yield, the cottagers being forced to do further work elsewhere to pay their rents. The Catholic Relief Act of 1793 resulted in land-division to increase voting strength, the vote being per household and the landlord expecting to receive it 'as part of the rent'. Cattle were seized for arrears of rent. In 1841 there were 500,000 families living in one-room mud cabins. The Irish were exploited to the limit, both as a class and as a nation.

The apathy after the '98 defeat lasted for some twenty years. During that time the old Catholic Committee still existed, but was inactive. In 1823 Daniel O'Connell revivified it with his Catholic Association, of which the parish priests were *ex officio* committee members, and to which every Catholic paid a shilling a year. O'Connell launched it at a favourable moment, when the ultra-reactionary Orange Order was a danger to the Whig Government, and the Association at first received official sanction; it was later banned, only to reappear under other names. O'Connell tested the discipline of his supporters at the Waterford election in 1826, succeeding in ousting the Beresford family from a seat they had held for seventy years, and then launched his Catholic Emancipation campaign. In 1829 every Catholic parish in Ireland petitioned for emancipation at the same hour on the same day. The Government was impressed. Then O'Connell was elected for Clare, and although the Orange faction threatened to 'kick the crown into the Boyne', emancipation was granted. Catholics were admitted to Parliament, to the Inner Bar and to commissions in the Services, and the fake voting system was abolished.

O'Connell took his seat at Westminster, where the struggle for the Reform Bill was going on. In Ireland, the Tithe War flamed up. Tithes were paid to the Protestant Church of Ireland—a parish with only four Protestant inhabitants, for example, gave a tithe revenue of over £200 a year. The tithe was often not one-tenth but one-quarter of the produce, and sometimes was more than the rent. The peasants were supporting the Protestant clergy as well as their own Catholic priesthood, and paying for the upkeep of Protestant as well as Catholic churches. The winning of emancipation, though it made no practical difference to the common people, had aroused a spirit of resistance. Strikes against the payment of tithes broke out all over Ireland and soon led to open fighting, especially in Kilkenny.

JOHNNY GREY

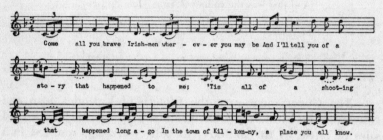

Come all you brave Irishmen wherever you may be
And I'll tell you a story that happened to me:
'Tis all of a shooting that happened long ago
In the town of Kilkenny, a place you all know.

Twas early one morning ere daylight did appear
Young Johnny went out his land for to clear
The Bailiff came on with his treacherous crew
Saying 'Johnny, the court has a warrant for you.

Your land will be taken to pay for your rent
And you'll be transported, your life to be spent
Far over the ocean in some foreign land
And from your own country forever you're banned.'

Young Johnny ran off to his house for his gun
'I'll not be transported whatever I've done!
I'll shoot the first traitor who crosses my gate
So go home to your Government before it's too late!'

The Bailiff gave orders to his Captain and crew:
'We'll surround this young Johnny, and shoot when I do—
Young Johnny, come out and surrender peacefully
Or soon you will swing from our high gallows tree!'

But the answer he gave them was fire and ball.
'My curse on all Bailiffs and traitors one and all!
I've tilled and I've worked every part of this land
And there's no one can shift me, I've taken my stand.'

The first shot was fired and the Captain fell dead.
The Bailiff said: 'Johnny, you heard what I said!
You'll swing from yon gallows, the highest you've seen
And the ravens of death will pick your bones clean.'

They surrounded the house and they held him at bay
And soon our Young Johnny all bleeding he lay.
With his last final shot, the Bailiff he did slay,
And that was the ending of Young Johnny Grey.

So come all you brave Irishmen wherever you may be:
Don't let them transport you all over the sea.
Stay in your own country and defend your own land
And soon we'll be free from this treacherous band.

The Government gave the Church of Ireland a loan and
converted the Tithe into a fixed annual payment, but the forced
sales of cattle by the military, to collect arrears, resulted in a
second wave of anti-tithe meetings and universal resistance.
Farm labourers and servants refused to work for anyone who did
not take a pledge not to collect tithes, and the people as a whole
refused to have any dealings with any auctioneer or purchaser of
seized cattle. The total abolition of the Tithe was demanded.

The Government's attempt to value farms in order to fix
the annual rate of payment was forcibly obstructed, the old
secret societies revived and the land war began again. Open
fighting went on from 1832 to 1834; at the last fight, the
collecting of forty shillings cost nineteen peasant lives and thirty-
five casualties, not counting the military. The fighting was
stopped by an enlightened Chief Secretary, Thomas Drummond,
who refused to use police or troops to collect arrears. The
Orange Order petitioned for his removal, but failed, and
Drummond dismissed all known Orangemen from the police-
force. At last in 1837 the Tithe was reduced by 25 per cent and
made payable by the landlords, many of whom prudently did not
attempt to recover it through increased rents.

Meanwhile O'Connell, in England, was proving bitterly
hostile to the Irish leaders of the Chartist movement, Doherty,
O'Connor and O'Brien. They had applauded the Tithe War,
whereas he tried to stop it. O'Connor was a descendant of one of
the United Irishmen, whose memory O'Connell execrated.
O'Connell was himself a landlord, and a fanatical hater of any
kind of revolution; he threw all his weight against Chartism. In

1841 he founded the Repeal Association (to end the Act of Union), and was faced with a problem when the Chartists supported it and still more when three of its members founded *The Nation* in 1842 and started what became known as the 'Young Ireland' movement. O'Connell's intention was to demand good government *or else* Repeal; but Young Ireland's interpretation was *Repeal or Separation*. O'Connell's personality and oratory at his monster meetings, backed by the persuasive clarity of *The Nation's* propaganda, roused the people further than he intended and drove him towards insurrection in spite of himself. Even magistrates and Orangemen began to join the Association. The Government brought in troops and proclaimed the All-Ireland rally at Clontarf (1843) illegal; and O'Connell, sure that the rally would be beyond his control, readily cancelled it.

O'Connell, Gavan Duffy and others were arrested and charged with forty-seven different seditious acts, six of which were publications in *The Nation*, one of these being John Kells Ingram's poem *The Memory Of The Dead* ('Who Fears to Speak of Ninety-Eight'). All were fined and sentenced to six months imprisonment, but the sentences were quashed by the House of Lords.

THE MEMORY OF THE DEAD

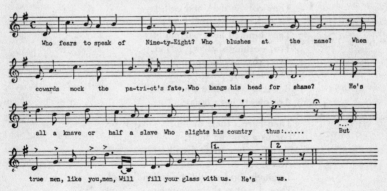

Who fears to speak of Ninety-Eight?
Who blushes at the name?
When cowards mock the patriot's fate,
Who hangs his head for shame?
He's all a knave or half a slave
Who slights his country thus:
But true men, like you men,
Will fill your glass with us.

We drink the memory of the brave
The faithful and the few—
Some lie far off beyond the wave,
Some sleep in Ireland too;
All, all are gone, but still lives on
The fame of those who died;
And true men, like you, men,
Remember them with pride.

Some on the shores of distant lands
Their weary hearts have laid,
And by the stranger's heedless hands
Their lonely graves were made;
But, though their clay be far away
Beyond the Atlantic foam,
In true men, like you, men,
Their spirit's still at home.

The dust of some is Irish earth;
Among their own they rest:
And the same land that gave them birth
Has caught them to her breast;
And we will pray that from their clay
Full many a race may start
Of true men, like you, men,
To act as brave a part.

They rose in dark and evil days
To right their native land;
They kindled here a living blaze
That nothing shall withstand.
Alas! that Might can vanquish Right—
They fell and passed away,
But true men, like you, men,
Are plenty here today.

Then here's their memory—may it be
For us a guiding light,
To cheer our strife for liberty
And teach us to unite!
Through good and ill, be Ireland's still,
Though sad as theirs your fate;
And true men be you, men,
Like those of Ninety-Eight.

John Kells Ingram

The Repeal Association declined, the fringe falling away
again and the militant nationalists losing confidence in O'Connell.
The latter did not encourage the Young Ireland policy of educating

the rank-and-file; he suddenly changed front and opposed the co-education of Protestant and Catholic in the Universities, now throwing all his 'moral force' in favour of sectarianism. This implied that Repeal would mean Catholic Ascendancy, and undermined *The Nation's* work for unity just when the movement was shaken by the untimley death of Davis at the age of thirty-one.

'Irish soil holds no more precious dust than this,' wrote *The Nation* in its report of Davis's funeral; '. . . the sun had gone out of the heavens,' said Gavin Duffy; '. . . the loss has never been repaired,' said John Mitchel. Many poems have been written in honour of Davis, Sir Samuel Ferguson's *Lament For Thomas Davis* being justly the most famous. But today he is perhaps best remembered for his own songs, still sung by Irishmen the world over. Here are two of the most popular.

NATIVE SWORDS

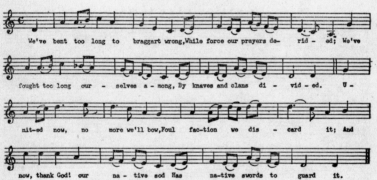

We've bent too long to braggart wrong,
While force our prayers derided;
We've fought too long, ourselves among,
By knaves and clans divided.
United now, no more we'll bow,
Foul faction we discard it;
And now thank God! our native sod
Has native swords to guard it.

Like rivers which, o'er valleys rich,
Bring ruin in their water,
On native land, a native hand
Flung foreign fraud and slaughter.
From Dermod's crime to Tudor's time
Our clans were our perdition;
Religion's name, since then, became
Our pretext for division.

But, worse than all, with Limerick's fall
Our valour seemed to perish;
Or o'er the main, in France and Spain,
For bootless vengeance flourish.
The peasant, here, grew pale for fear
He'd suffer for our glory,
While France sang joy for Fontenoy,
And Europe hymned our story.

But now, no clan, nor factious plan,
The East and West can sunder—
Why Ulster e'er should Munster fear,
Can only make us wonder.
Religion's crost, when union's lost,
And 'royal gifts' retard it;
But now, thank God! our native sod
Has native swords to guard it.

Thomas Davis

A NATION ONCE AGAIN

When boyhood's fire was in my blood,
I read of ancient freemen,
For Greece and Rome who bravely stood,
Three hundred men and three men.
And then I prayed I yet might see
Our fetters rent in twain,
And Ireland, long a province, be
A nation once again.

A nation once again,
A nation once again!
And Ireland, long a province, be
A nation once again!

And, from that time, through wildest woe,
That hope has shone, a far light;
Nor could love's brightest summer glow
Outshine that solemn starlight:
It seemed to watch above my head
In forum, field and fane;
Its angel voice sang round my bed,
'A nation once again.'

Chorus

It whispered, too, that 'freedom's ark
And service high and holy,
Would be profaned by feelings dark
And passions vain or lowly:
For freedom comes from God's right hand,
And needs a godly train;
And righteous men must make our land
A nation once again.'

Chorus

So, as I grew from boy to man,
I bent me to that bidding—
My spirit of each selfish plan
And cruel passion ridding;
For, thus I hoped some day to aid—
Oh! can such hope be vain?
When my dear country shall be made
A nation once again.
        A nation once again,
        A nation once again!
        And Ireland, long a province, be
        A nation once again!

                            Thomas Davis

From 1845 to 1848 the national movement staggered some-
how through the Famine years. What the Irish of the time called
the Starvation (for there *was* food in Ireland, except potatoes)
was partial in 1845, general in 1846 and universal in 1847. The
scenes of horror beggar all description. The Introduction to
Mitchel's *Jail Journal* describes how 'families, when all was eaten

and no hope left, took their last look at the sun, built up their cottage doors, that none might see them die nor hear their groans, and were found weeks afterwards, skeletons on their own hearth'.

> So hie thee to our cabin lone, and dig a grave so deep,
> And underneath the golden gorse our corpses lay to sleep—
> Else they will come and smash the walls upon our mould'ring bones
> And screaming mountain birds will tear our flesh from out the stones.

It tells, too, how 'starving wretches were transported for stealing vegetables', and 'overworked coroners declared they would hold no more inquests', while 'in every one of those years Ireland was exporting to England food to the value of £15,000,000, and had on her own soil at each harvest good and ample provision for double her own population'; and 'the high aspirations after a national senate and a national flag had sunk to a mere craving for food'.

Ireland, like the rest of Europe, had an insurrection in 1848, for, as the *Jail Journal* Introduction says, 'even as she was, depopulated, starved, cowed and corrupted, it seemed better that she should attempt resistance, however heavy the odds against success, than lie prostrate and moaning as she was'.

THE FAMINE SONG

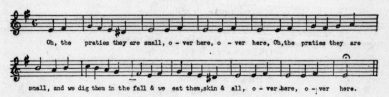

Oh, the praties they are small, o - ver here, o - ver here, Oh, the praties they are small, and we dig them in the fall & we eat them, skin & all, o - ver here, o - ver here.

> Oh, the praties they are small, over here, over here,
> Oh the praties they are small and we dig them in the Fall
> And we eat them skin and all, over here, over here.
>
> Oh, we wish that we were geese, night and morn, night and morn,
> Oh, we wish that we were geese and could live our lives in peace
> Till the hour of our release, eating corn, eating corn.
>
> Oh, we're down into the dust, over here, over here,
> Oh, we're down into the dust, but the Lord in whom we trust
> Will repay us crumb for crust, over here, over here.

The people's enfeebled condition, coupled with confusion of leadership and contradictory instructions, inevitably resulted in the failure of the 1848 insurrection and wholesale arrests and transportation (including that of John Mitchel). Once again Ireland lapsed into a temporary apathy broken only by the regular departure of the emigrant death-ships, on which typhus claimed almost as many victims as the Famine itself.

JOHN MITCHEL

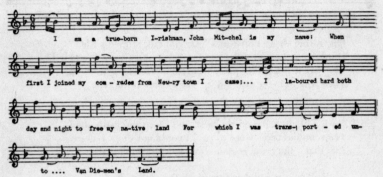

I am a true-born Irishman, John Mitchel is my name:
When first I joined my comrades from Newry town I came;
I laboured hard both day and night to free my native land
For which I was transported unto Van Dieman's Land.

When first I joined my countrymen it was in '42;
And what did happen after that I'll quickly tell to you;
I raised the standard of Repeal, I gloried in the deed;
I vowed to heaven I ne'er would rest till Old Ireland would be freed.

Farewell my gallant comrades, it grieves my heart full sore
To think that I must part from you, perhaps for evermore;
The love I bear my native land, I know no other crime;
That is the reason I must go into a foreign clime.

As I lay in strong irons bound, before my trial day
My loving wife came to my cell, and thus to me did say:
'Oh, John, my dear, cheer up your heart, undaunted always be,
For it's better to die for Erin's rights than live in slavery.'

I was placed on board a convict ship without the least delay;
For Bermuda's Isle our course was steered: I'll ne'er forget the day,
As I stood upon the deck to take a farewell view
I shed a tear, but not for fear; my native land, for you.

Adieu! Adieu! to sweet Belfast, and likewise Dublin too,
And to my young and tender babes; alas, what will they do?
But there's one request I ask of you, when your liberty you gain
Remember John Mitchel far away, though a convict bound in chains.

SKIBBEREEN

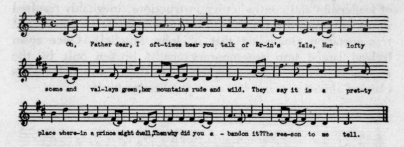

Oh, Father dear, I oft-times hear you talk of Erin's Isle,
Her lofty scene and valleys green, her mountains rude and wild,
They say it is a pretty place wherein a prince might dwell,
Then why did you abandon it? The reason to me tell.

My son, I loved our native land with energy and pride
Until a blight came on the land, and sheep and cattle died,
The rent and taxes were to pay, I could not them redeem,
And that's the cruel reason why I left old Skibbereen.

It's well I do remember that bleak December day
The landlord and the sheriff came to drive us all away,
They set my roof on fire with their demon yellow spleen,
And that's another reason why I left old Skibbereen.

It's well I do remember the year of forty-eight,
When I arose with Erin's boys to fight against the fate,
I was hunted through the mountains for a traitor to the Queen,
And that's another reason why I left old Skibbereen.

Oh, Father dear, the day will come when vengeance loud will call,
And we will rise with Erin's boys and rally one and all,
I'll be the man to lead the van beneath our flag of green,
And loud and high we'll raise the cry: 'Revenge for Skibbereen!'

The Fenians

The famine and the mass emigrations had eliminated large
numbers of smallholders and middlemen. In the ten years
1841-51, the number of holdings of less than one acre fell from
over 135,000 to about 37,000; between one acre and five,
from over 300,000 to 88,000; between five acres and fifteen,
from over 250,000 to about 190,000. Larger farms, however,
increased in number, especially those of more than thirty acres.

At the same time the eviction figures multiplied: 3,000 in 1845-7; over 25,000 in 1847-9; over 58,000 in 1849-52. This last figure affected more than 300,000 persons.

That is to say, the Famine helped to precipitate the establishment in Ireland of large-scale capitalist farming and to transform the peasantry into an agricultural labourer class. The sale of encumbered estates to speculators increased rack-renting and abolished traditional tenants' rights, leases being replaced by tenancies-at-will. Virtually the entire rural population became evictable.

The Irish peasantry still retained in practice some of the ancient Gaelic rights of tenure; in particular, the acceptance of a rent tribute was a recognition of the *tenant's right of tenure*. The new capitalist concept, that the payment of rent was a recognition of the *landlord's* right, was totally alien to tradition and custom. In brief, the Irish had no concept of 'Free Trade', now the gospel of the authorities.

The agrarian secret societies reappeared, demanding 'the three Fs': fixity of tenure, fair rent, free sale (of the tenant's own improvements). They were supported by the constitutional agitation led by Gavan Duffy in the re-created *Nation* (1850) and in the Tenants' Right League (1852), which demanded reform by means of a Land Act. In this agitation, North and South joined hands without regard to denomination, to the extent of Catholic priests seconding resolutions proposed by Orangemen. The Parliamentary candidates of the Catholic Defence Association (at the 1852 election), led by William Keogh and John Sadleir—although at the same time they were encouraging sectarianism—pledged support to Tenants' Right demands. Nearly fifty Tenants' Right supporters were returned to Westminster, where they held the balance of power between Whig and Tory; two Tenants' Right Bills went forward. But Keogh and Sadleir were offered, and accepted, Ministerial appointments; they took almost half their supporters with them to the Government side of the House.

The Tenants' Right Bills were dropped at once; Irish landlords, the Catholic hierarchy, the heads of the Orange Order, and the British government, united to denounce the League by the new term of abuse, 'communistic'. The parish priests and young curates who had been working for the League were ordered by the cardinal and by their bishops to confine themselves strictly to their spiritual functions. Duffy gave up the struggle and emigrated to Australia. Sadleir, guilty of financial fraud, committed suicide (at midnight, on Hampstead Heath). Keogh, however, became Lord Chief Justice of Ireland.

Sporadic agrarian terrorism continued, but the next few years were otherwise blank, until returning exiles brought fresh hope of renewed struggle. Three of the '48 men, Doheny, O'Mahoney and Stephens, reached America in 1856 from Paris, where they had been much impressed by Blanqui's technique of disciplined secret conspiracy. They conceived the idea of the Fenian Brotherhood (named after the legendary hero Finn McColl), with a secret oath-bound 'hard core', the Irish Republican Brotherhood. In 1857 Stephens visited Ireland and got in touch with the secret Phoenix Society, led by O'Donovan Rossa ; but information was laid and the Phoenix leaders were arrested. Fenian recruiting, however, went on in America on a large scale, especially among the Irish Brigade (under Meagher, a '48 exile) in the Northern Army in the American Civil War—a period when Irish emigration to America increased noticeably. A fund was raised in America to purchase a ship, the Erin's Hope, which sailed for Ireland and landed a few dozen men illicitly in 1867, but made no further trips.

THE FENIAN MAN O' WAR

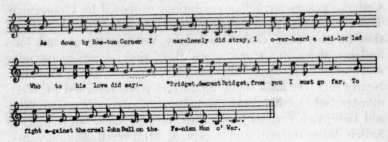

Down by Boston Corner I carelessly did stray,
I overheard a sailor lad these words to his love did say—
Bridget, dearest Bridget, from you I must go far,
To fight against the cruel John Bull on the Fenian Man o' War.

Oh, Patrick, dearest Patrick, don't go away from me,
For the English they are treacherous as ever they can be,
And by some cruel dagger you might receive a scar.
Oh, Patrick, dear, don't venture near the Fenian Man o' War.

When I think on the days gone by, my heart with joy does fill,
To see the thousands of people all assembled on Vinegar Hill.
They were holding a prayer meeting for the dead who were buried afar,
And you could hear the cannons roar of a Fenian Man o'War.

I was born in the Bogside, I hate those English laws,
My parents they were Irish and they died for an Irish cause;
If ever I go to visit them from thousands of miles afar,
It will be for dear old Ireland's sake and a Fenian Man o'War.

Oh, Bridget, dearest Bridget, the truth to you I'll tell,
The English were insulted and the Irish knew it well,
They might make of me a captain instead of a common tar,
So I'll risk my life for Ireland's rights on board the Man o'War.

They both sat down together, then he arose to stand,
A Fenian crew surrounded them, which nearly rowed to land,
Then Patrick raised a Fenian flag and waved it near and far,
And Bridget blessed her sailor boy on board the Man o'War.

In 1863 the Fenian journal, the *Irish People*, appeared in
Dublin; it was edited by Luby and O'Leary, with the help of
Kickham and O'Donovan Rossa. The violent denunciations with
which it was greeted served only to increase its popularity. In
1865 the ending of the American Civil War demobilized
200,000 Irish-American Fenians. The *Irish People* was raided and
its leaders were arrested. Stephens escaped (with the help of
Fenian warders); Devoy urged immediate insurrection, but
Stephens and the Americans insisted on delay. The arrested
leaders were brought to trial before Keogh, who inflicted savage
sentences of twenty years on Luby, O'Leary and Kickham and of
life on Rossa. Devoy was arrested and Stephens proved ineffective
in leadership. In America the movement split and split again as a
result of inconclusive delays.

In 1867 a rising was planned, at first for February, then for
March; Kerry and the North of England were not informed of
the change of date, rose too soon and thus gave warning to the
authorities. In addition, the March 'rising' coincided with an
exceptionally violent blizzard. There was practically no fighting.
The Fenian military leaders, Kelley and Deasy, were arrested in
Manchester, but daringly rescued, a policeman being killed.
The rescuers, Allen, Larkin and O'Brien, were hanged, and are
known to history as the Manchester Martyrs. (Ernest Jones,
the Chartist, as defence counsel, threw down his brief in protest at the court's refusal to remove the prisoners' handcuffs in
the dock.) The celebrated song *God Save Ireland*, written in

their honour, was for fifty years Ireland's unofficial national anthem. (See Supplement, page 83.)

THE SMASHING OF THE VAN

At — tend you gal-lant Irish-men and lis-ten for a while....... I'll sing to you the prais-es of the sons of Er-in's Isle; It's of those gal-lant he-roes who vol-un-tari-ly ran To re — lease two Irish Fe-ni-ans from an Eng-lish pri-son van..........

Attend you gallant Irishmen and listen for a while
I'll sing to you the praises of the sons of Erin's Isle
It's of those gallant heroes who voluntarily ran
To release two Irish Fenians from an English prison van.

On the eighteenth of September, it was a dreadful year,
When sorrow and excitement ran throughout all Lancashire,
At a gathering of the Irish boys they volunteered each man,
To release those Irish prisoners out of the prison van.

Kelly and Deasy were their names, I suppose you knew them well,
Remanded for a week they were in Bellevue Gaol to dwell,
When taking of the prisoners back, their trial for to stand,
To make a safe deliverance they conveyed them in a van.

William Deasy was a man of good and noted fame,
Likewise Michael Larkin, we'll never forget his name,
With young Allen and O'Brien they took a part so grand,
In that glorious liberation and the smashing of the van.

In Manchester one morning those heroes did agree,
Their leaders, Kelly and Deasy, should have their liberty,
They drank a health to Ireland, and soon made up the plan,
To meet the prisoners on the road and take and smash the van.

With courage bold those heroes went and soon the van did stop,
They cleared the guards from back and front and then smashed
                                                  in the top,
But in blowing open of the lock, they chanced to kill a man,
So three must die on the scaffold high for smashing of the van.

One cold November morning in eighteen sixty-seven
These martyrs to their country's cause a sacrifice were given,
'God save Ireland,' was the cry, all through the crowd it ran,
The Lord have mercy on the boys that helped to smash the van.

So now kind friends I will conclude, I think it would be right
That all true-hearted Irishmen together should unite,
Together should sympathize, my friends, and do the best we can
To keep the memories ever green, of the boys that smashed the van.

Late in the year, a few Fenian sympathizers, on their own
initiative, attempted another rescue in London; they succeeded
only in blowing up the wall of Clerkenwell Prison and wrecking a
street, killing seven people and injuring 120. This futile and
irresponsible act showed the rapid degeneration of the movement,
and alienated or bewildered many English sympathizers. Nevertheless, the untiring efforts of the International Working Men's
Association and the Fenian Amnesty Movement secured the
release of most of the leading Fenians in 1871.

The importance of the Fenian movement lies in its representation of the aims of the United Irishmen; in its manifesta-
tion to the whole world of Ireland's demand for complete
independence; in its reintroduction of Irish claims into the
programme of progressive movements in England; in its absolute
rejection of sectarianism; in its standard of complete fidelity and
steadfastness, of disciplined manliness; in its unmistakably
democratic character and intentions. That its enemies well
understood its potential is plainly demonstrated by the famous and
appalling dictum that *Hell is not hot enough, nor Eternity long enough,
to punish the Fenians.*

THE BOLD FENIAN MEN

See who comes o-ver the red-blossomed heather, Their green ban-ners
kissing the pure mountain air, Heads e-rect, eyes to front, stepping proud-ly together, Sure free-dom sits throned on each proud spi-rit there. Down the hill
twin-ing, Their bless-ed steel shin-ing, Like rivers of beau-ty that flow from each
glen, From moun-tain and val-ley, 'Tis Li-ber-ty's ral-ly— Out and make
way for the bold Fe-nian men. Our

See who comes over the red-blossomed heather,
Their green banners kissing the pure mountain air,
Heads erect, eyes to front, stepping proudly together,
Sure freedom sits throned on each proud spirit there.
Down the hill twining,
Their blessed steel shining,
Like rivers of beauty that flow from each glen,
From mountain and valley,
'Tis Liberty's rally—
Out and make way for the bold Fenian men!

Our prayers and our tears they have scoffed and derided,
They've shut out the sunlight from spirit and mind.
Our foes were united and we were divided,
We met and they scattered our ranks to the wind.
But once more returning,
Within our veins burning
The fires that illumined dark Aherlow glen;
We raise the old cry anew,
Slogan of Conn and Hugh;
Out and make way for the bold Fenian men!

We've men from the Nore, from the Suir and the Shannon,
Let tyrants come forth, we'll bring force against force,
Our pen is the sword and our voice is the cannon,
Rifle for rifle and horse against horse.
We've made the false Saxon yield
Many a red battlefield:
God on our side, we will triumph again;
Pay them back woe for woe ,
Give them back blow for blow—
Out and make way for the bold Fenian men!

Side by side for the cause have our forefathers battled,
When our hills never echoed the tread of a slave;
In many a field where the leaden hail rattled,
Through the red gap of glory they marched to the grave.
And those who inherit
Their name and their spirit,
Will march 'neath the banners of Liberty then;
All who love foreign law—
Native or Sasanach—
Must out and make way for the bold Fenian Men!

Michael Scanlan

Parliament and Land League

In 1869 (thirty-five years after the Tithe War), Gladstone's
Government dis-established the Protestant Church of Ireland
and then embarked on a series of Land Acts (twelve between 1870

and 1909) aimed at redressing major grievances. These Acts were attacked as interfering with property rights, and were sabotaged by landlords. Further clearances of smallholders were made, and rents increased while prices for agricultural products fell.

The agitation for the Fenian Amnesty had grown into a demand for Home Rule, and soon created an Irish nationalist Parliamentary Party. Sixty Home Rule members were elected in 1874; at a by-election in 1875 Parnell was elected for Meath, and almost at once, in conjunction with Joseph Biggar, developed the tactic of 'obstructionism' as a means of publicising their denial of Britain's right to legislate for Ireland. For the first time Irish Members intervened in English affairs, insisting on complete independence for their country or else unlimited delays and impediments at Westminster. The Irish question was brought sharply home to the authorities on their own doorstep.

In Ireland, in 1879, Michael Davitt (a Fenian leader) founded the Land League, for the purpose of resisting eviction, and Parnell agreed to head it. Most of the Fenian leaders agreed to the 'New Departure' of coupling militant action with Parliamentary debate (while still keeping the 'underground' organization in existence), and national unity was once more largely achieved.

There followed ten years of brilliant political pincer-movements by Davitt and the agrarian militants on the one hand and Parnell and the Parliamentary obstructionists on the other, countered by alternate (or sometimes simultaneous) coercion and concession on the part of the Government. The Irish frequently held the balance of power in the House of Commons, and used it as a weapon. Throughout this period a land war was going on, in the form of active resistance to eviction and of rent-strikes. Parnell invented the use of social ostracism as a political weapon, which within three days of his famous speech at Clare became known to Britain (and ultimately to the world) as 'boycott'. He was arrested but released under an agreement of moderation in return for no-coercion and the waiving of rent arrears. The agreement was strangled at birth by the 'Phoenix Park murders', the sudden assassination of the Lord Lieutenant and the Chief Secretary by members of a secret 'splinter group'.

Parnell's importance may be gauged by the great lengths to which his enemies went to 'down' him. The Phoenix Park assassinations were laid at his door; the *Times* published forged letters purporting to implicate him in terrorist acts; the 'framed' divorce case at last smashed his political career and broke his heart. The intense bitterness of hostility against him derives from the dual facts that he brought Irish affairs red-hot into British domestic politics, and that his brilliant Parliamentary activities were closely integrated with the active resistance of the common people.

From Parnell to the Easter Rising

After Parnell there was a lull during which various Land Acts were passed and the trade union and socialist movements were slowly extending. The Parliamentary nationalist party degenerated; the Gaelic League grew and Sinn Fein made its appearance.

The third Home Rule Bill in 1911 was the first introduced after the abolition of the House of Lords veto, and was obviously likely to become law. The Belfast Tories, alarmed by the possibilities of unity between Nationalist Republicans and Socialist Republicans, began to insist on the separation of Northern Ireland. The great Dublin transport strike of 1913, led by James Connolly and Jim Larkin, intensified their fears and hostility.

> Who fears to wear the blood-red badge
> Upon his manly breast?
> What scab obeys the vile command
> Of Murphy and the rest?
> He's all a knave and half a slave
> Who slights his Union thus,
> But true men like you men
> Will show the badge with us.
>
> They dared to fling a manly brick,
> They wrecked a blackleg tram.
> They dared give Harvey Duff a kick,
> They didn't give a damn.
> They lie in jail and can't get bail,
> Who fought their corner thus;
> But you men, with sticks, men,
> Must make the peelers cuss.

Anti-Home Rule Volunteer drilling and gun-running began in Northern Ireland, where Carson announced a provisional

government. A volunteer force was formed in Dublin to defend
Home Rule. Only then did the Government prohibit the import
of arms into Ireland. The Carsonites landed a large cargo of
German arms at Larne early in 1914, and the Ulster Volunteers
paraded armed in Belfast. The Irish Volunteers landed 1,000
rifles in Dublin, and British troops unsuccessfully attempted to
seize them; in disturbances later that day three people were shot
dead in Batchelor's Walk.

BATCHELOR'S WALK

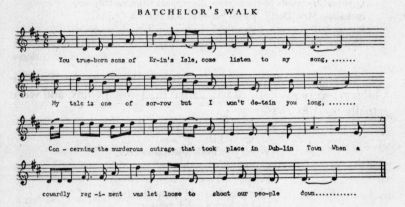

You true-born sons of Er-in's Isle, come listen to my song, ...
My tale is one of sor-row but I won't de-tain you long, ...
Con - cerning the murderous outrage that took place in Dub-lin Town When a
cowardly reg -i- ment was let loose to shoot our peo-ple down............

You true-born sons of Erin's Isle, come listen to my song,
My tale is one of sorrow but I won't detail you long,
Concerning the murderous outrage that took place in Dublin Town
When a cowardly regiment was let loose to shoot our people down.

On the 26th day of July, the truth I'll tell to you,
The Irish Volunteers all swore their enemies to subdue,
They marched straight out to Howth and soon the people were alarmed
When they heard the glorious new 'Our Irish Volunteers are armed'.

The crowds they all kept cheering on as our brave defenders passed
But their cheers were stopped by an outrage which for some time did last.
Our gallant men, the Volunteers, were met in front and rear,
By the King's Own Scottish cowards who are doomed for everywhere.

God save our gallant Captain Judge, the hero of the band
Who nearly gave his precious life for the just cause of our land
In spite of terrible injuries and weak from loss of blood,
He fondly hugged his rifle grand the prize of his brotherhood.

Next in the list of heroes is the scout so well renowned,
With the butt end of his rifle felled a Borderer to the ground,
He disarmed him of his weapons and soon made his escape,
By climbing a wall in Fairview, for his young life was at stake.

The Dublin Police were ordered the Volunteers for to subdue,
But O'Neill and Gleeson boldly replied: 'Such a thing we decline to do,
For to fight against our countrymen would on us put a stain,
For we wish to see our native land a Nation Once Again'.

On Batchelor's Walk a scene took place, which I'm sure had just been
                                                               planned,
For the cowardly Scottish Borderers turned and fired without command.
With bayonets fixed they charged the crowd and left them in their gore,
But their deeds will be remembered in Irish hearts for evermore.

God rest the souls of those who sleep apart from earthly sin,
Including Mrs. Duffy, James Brennan and Patrick Quinn;
But we will yet avenge them and the time will surely come,
That we'll make the Scottish Borderers pay for the cowardly deeds they
                                                               done.

These guns (brought into Howth Harbour by Erskine Childers) were ever afterwards called the Howth Guns, and were actually used in 1916.

> How glorious was your feel,
> O, my old Howth Gun!
> When you made the Saxon reel,
> O, my old Howth Gun!
> When the Lancers, trim and neat,
> Charging down O'Connell Street,
> Had to beat a quick retreat,
> O, my old Howth Gun!

When the European war broke out, the Home Rule Bill was suspended 'for the duration'.

'The Troubles,' 1916-23

At the outbreak of World War I there were in Ireland a number of organizations pledged to the achievement of an independent Irish Republic. The *Gaelic League* was working to sustain the spirit of nationhood by reviving the Irish language and studying ancient and traditional Irish customs and culture, with a view to a Gaelic Republic; the *Sinn Fein* ('Ourselves Alone') party stood for complete political and economic separation from England, rather than mere 'Home Rule' (i.e. Dominion status); the *Irish Volunteers* to an extent were directed by the rump of the Fenian Brotherhood (whose oath was life-long and whose inner circle, the I.R.B., continued to exist); Larkin's 'army' of the Transport Union, a disciplined body of workers formed during the great 1913 strike to defend union platforms against assault, had continued in being as the *Citizen Army*, commanded by James Connolly and recruited solely from trade union members; the *Socialist Republican Party*, also led by Connolly, declared for an independent Workers' Socialist Republic. The Gaelic League, Sinn Fein, the I.R.B. and the Volunteers recruited among all shades of political opinion; a trade unionist might well belong to any or all of them as well as to the Citizen Army.

At first, the fact that Home Rule had actually been granted (for after the war), served to allay open hostility to Britain; but the Parliamentary Party (under Redmond) split the nation by its pledge of support to the British Government and aroused fears of the possible conscription of Irishmen into the British forces. The I.R.B., Sinn Fein and the Socialists all opposed any Irish participation in the war, boycotting and demonstrating against recruiting rallies.

> For hail or rain or frost or snow,
> We're not going out to Flanders, O,
> While there's fighting to be done at home.
> Let your privates and commanders go.
> Let Englishmen for England fight;
> It's nearly time they started, O!

Connolly's writings in *The Workers' Republic* (printed on its own press under an armed Citizen Army guard) became more and more militant and 'seditious'. The I.R.B. invited him to bring his forces into their plans for an armed rising at Easter, 1916, and he became a member of the I.R.B. War Directory.

Among the secret plans was the project of an Irish Brigade formed of prisoners-of-war in Germany; Sir Roger Casement failed to form this, but did obtain arms, which were however intercepted by the British. The car sent to meet Casement crashed over a cliff; Casement was captured and hanged in London for treason.

LONELY BANNA STRAND

'Twas on Good Friday morn-ing all in the month of May, A Ger-man ship was sig-nalling be-yond there in the Bay, "We've twenty-thousand ri-fles here, all ready for to land." But no answ'ring signal came from the lonely Ban-na Strand.

'Twas on Good Friday morning all in the month of May
A German ship was signalling beyond there in the Bay,
'We've twenty thousand rifles here, all ready for to land'.
But no answering signal came from the lonely Banna Strand.

A motor-car was dashing through the early morning gloom
A sudden crash, and in the stream they went to meet their doom,
Two Irish lads lay dying there just like their hopes so grand,
They could not give the signal now from lonely Banna Strand.

'No signal answers from the shore' Sir Roger sadly said,
'No comrades here to welcome me, alas, they must be dead,
But I must do my duty and at once I mean to land'.
So in a boat he pulled ashore to lonely Banna Strand.

The German ships were lying there with rifles in galore
Up came a British ship and spoke, 'No Germans reach the shore;
You are our Empire's enemy, and so we bid you stand
No German foot shall e'er pollute the lonely Banna Strand.'

They sailed for Queenstown Harbour. Said the Germans 'We're
                                                                    undone,
The British are our masters man for man and gun for gun,
We've twenty thousand rifles here, but they never will reach land
We'll sink them all and bid farewell to lonely Banna Strand.'

The R.I.C. were hunting for Sir Roger high and low
They found him at McKenna's Fort, said they 'You are our foe'.
Said he, 'I'm Roger Casement, I came to my native land,
I meant to free my countrymen on the lonely Banna Strand.'

They took Sir Roger prisoner and sailed for London Town,
And in the Tower they laid him as a traitor to the Crown,
Said he, 'I am no traitor' but his trial he had to stand
For bringing German rifles to the lonely Banna Strand.

'Twas in an English prison that they led him to his death
'I'm dying for my country' he said with his last breath
He's buried in a prison yard far from his native land
The wild waves sing his Requiem on the Lonely Banna Strand.

At the same time the Rebellion broke out in Dublin, not on
Easter Sunday as planned, but (owing to confusion of orders and
authority) on Easter Monday. The delay and confusion hampered
a general rising, and the fighting was largely confined to Dublin,
where a contingent of Citizen Army and Volunteers seized the
General Post Office (in the centre of the city), hoisted the
Republican flag and proclaimed a sovereign independent Irish
Republic.

O, the night fell black and the rifles' crack made 'Perfidious Albion' reel,
'Mid the leaden rain seven tongues of flame did shine o'er the lines of steel ;
By each shining blade a prayer was said that to Ireland her sons be true,
And when morning broke still the war flag shook out its folds in the Foggy Dew.

After a week's hard fighting the Rebellion as such was crushed and local outbreaks in Galway, Meath and Wexford subsided. All seven signatories of the Proclamation (the Provisional Government: Clarke, MacDermott, MacDonagh, Pearse, Kent, Connolly and Plunkett) with eight others (Daly, O'Hanrahan, W. Pearse, MacBride, Mallin, Colbert, Heuston, T. Kent) were executed on 3rd-12th May. These, with Casement, are the Sixteen Dead Men of 1916, famed in song and poem.

When the executions were announced to the House of Commons by Asquith, not only Tories and Liberals, but Irish Redmondite M.P's, rose and cheered.

O did you hear the Members cheering, cheering?
O did you hear the Members cheering?
As Asquith told them of the shooting, shooting
The Irish scum that stopped recruiting,
When Paddy Pearse fought and died
And noble Plunkett lost his bride—
To set the Members cheering, cheering!
Sure soldiers must be shooting, shooting,
To cool such wicked Irish pride.
Ye'll not forget the Members cheering!

Scores of others were condemned, but world public opinion brought about the release, first of those still untried and then of those already convicted. Volunteer drilling and demonstrating began again, with hundreds of further arrests. Prisoners (taking example from the Suffragettes, with whom Constance Gore-Booth, now Countess Markiewicz, Treasurer of the Citizen Army, had worked) began to go on hunger-strike. Thomas Ashe died on hunger-strike and was given a military funeral by the I.R.B. The only surviving Easter Week Commandant, De Valera, was elected President of the Sinn Fein party, which now incorporated Republicans and Nationalists of every shade, its Executive Committee being recognized in Ireland as a *de facto* Government.

Meanwhile the Northern reactionaries, with the support of the British authorities, were demanding that the Home Rule Bill be amended to exclude North East Ulster (six counties of the nine that make up the province of Ulster). In 1918 conscription was at last imposed on Ireland; and even mild Irish M.P.'s. left Westminster in a body and 'went Sinn Fein'. All sections of nationalist Ireland were solidly together against conscription. The Sinn Fein leaders were arrested. The unions called a token General Strike. At the General Election in December, 1918, Sinn Fein won almost every seat in Ireland.

The Sinn Fein M.P.'s. (except for those who were in gaol or 'on the run') met in Dublin and declared themselves the governing body of the Republic established in Easter Week, under the name Dail Eireann (the Assembly of Ireland), with Cathal Brugha—who had fought in 1916—as acting President pending De Valera's return from gaol. (He escaped from Lincoln Prison in February, 1919.)

The British Government declared the Dail illegal and all its works seditious. Almost every prominent nationalist was on the run or in prison. Elaborate intelligence services were developed on both sides, and the whole machinery of government administration was 'illegally' duplicated by Sinn Fien local councils, courts and so on. Some of the Volunteers adopted the old Fenian name of Irish Republican Army, and maintained incessant partisan warfare in defence of the Republic and its Assembly.

The Volunteer movement retained its independent initiative and tactics, with the general sanction of the Dail. Innumerable local guerilla engagements went on. The following is famous. In April, 1919, a small group of Volunteers, led by Sean Treacy and Sean Hogan, ambushed and captured a load of gelignite, two policemen being killed in the skirmish. Hogan was arrested, but on his way to be tried a month later was rescued by Treacy at Knocklong, two more policemen being shot. (Treacy was later killed in a lone battle in Dublin in 1920. See p. 65.).

THE STATION OF KNOCKLONG

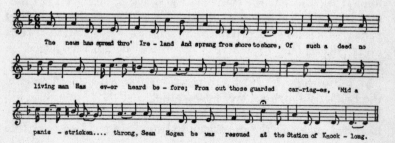

The news has spread thro' Ire-land And sprang from shore to shore, Of such a deed no living man Has ev-er heard be-fore; From out those guarded car-riag-es, 'Mid a panic - stricken.... throng, Sean Hogan he was rescued at the Station of Knock-long.

The news has spread through Ireland,
And sprang from shore to shore,
Of such a deed no living man
Has ever heard before;
From out those guarded carriages,
Mid a panic-stricken throng,
Sean Hogan he was rescued,
At the Station of Knocklong.

With a guard of four policemen,
And their prisoner minded well,
As that fatal train sped o'er the rails,
Conveying him to his cell;
The prisoner then could scarce foretell
Of hearts both brave and strong,
That were planning for his rescue
At the Station of Knocklong.

'Twas on a gloomy evening,
When at last the train pulled in,
It was halted for an hour or more
By a few courageous men;
Then springing to the carriages,
It did not take them long,
'Hands up or die' was the warning cry,
At the Station of Knocklong.

King George's pampered hirelings
They shrivelled up with fear,
When they thought of how they'd placed in cells
Full many a Volunteer;
Now face to face with armed men,
To escape how did they long,
But two of them met traitors' deaths
At the Station of Knocklong.

From Solohead to Limerick,
Such deeds as these were seen,
And the devil a tear was ever shed
For Wallace or Rosegreen;
They did old England's dirty work
But they did that work too long,
For the renegades were numbered,
At the Station of Knocklong.

Now rise up Mother Erin,
And always be of cheer,
You ne'er shall die while by your side
There stand such Volunteers;

> From Dingle Bay to Garryowen,
> The cheers they'll echo long,
> Of the rescue of Sean Hogan
> At the Station of Knocklong.

Many counties and cities were now under martial law and protest strikes were called. There were countless ambushes, rescues, and reprisals, as well as wholesale arrests and detention (including solitary confinement) without trial.

American delegates visited Ireland. The U.S. Senate passed a resolution calling on the American Commission at the Versailles Peace Conference to try to get a hearing at the Conference for Irish delegates to state Ireland's case; but this was vetoed by President Wilson. Meanwhile Dublin was an armed camp. The Irish Bishops denounced the British regime as 'the rule of the sword'. The army of occupation was costing Britain £10,800,000 a year. Lord Carson threatened to call out the Orange Volunteers if Home Rule was applied to the North; Lloyd George then said there could be no settlement till the Irish agreed among themselves (in spite of the overwhelming Sinn Fein majority at the election).

> Oh! bring out the Volunteers
> And Carson's gang of Peers
> And we'll fight them all from Dublin
> To Cape Clear.
> We've the National Brigade
> And we'll never be afraid,
> And we're going to have Home Rule,
> For Ireland dear.

The Times said: 'The hope that an army of military force might cow the Irish . . . has plainly miscarried.' British civil administration had completely broken down.

Guerilla warfare increased in violence and in extent. Michael Collins organized a highly efficient counter-espionage network. British regular troops sacked Fermoy. Virtually the whole population aided and abetted, sheltered and protected the Volunteers and the I.R.B. The British prohibited Dail Eireann. De Valera left for America to raise a loan; Britain sent her publicists there too, but with little effect. Military aggression against the civil population in Ireland increased into an actual reign of terror. The Dail met in secret. Every day had its tale of horror, even children being shot. Regular troops sacked Cork

City. A Sinn Fein *Bulletin* appeared and circulated secretly. The police were armed with hand-grenades.

At the municipal elections in January, 1920, Sinn Fein swept the country (including five of the nine countries of Ulster). From 172 newly-elected Councils (out of the total of 206) came resolutions of allegiance to the Republic and the Dail. The regime of oppression was intensified; that month over 1,000 raids were made. The Bishops protested. Volunteers' attacks and ambushes continued, still always with the purpose of obtaining supplies of arms or of rescuing prisoners. A Curfew Order was imposed in several cities. Thurles and Cork were wrecked by police assaults. Thomas McCurtain, Lord Mayor of Cork, was shot dead by night in his own home; the coroner's jury returned a verdict of *Wilful murder by the Royal Constabulary, officially directed by the British Government.*

A new force was recruited in England (at high pay), the 'auxiliaries' or 'specials' known to history as the Black-and-Tans (they wore khaki jackets and black trousers) or more simply the Tans. Technically they were a reserve police force, but in reality they were what the next generation came to know as fascist stormtroopers. Their activities sickened the world and aroused widespread sympathy for the Irish people and support for the Irish cause.

THE BOLD BLACK AND TAN

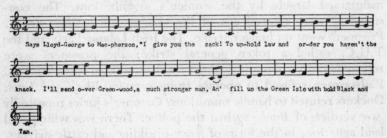

Says Lloyd-George to Macpherson, 'I give you the sack,
To uphold law and order you haven't the knack,
I'll send over Greenwood, a much stronger man,
And fill up the Green Isle with the bold Black and Tan.'

He sent them all over to pillage and loot
And burn down the houses, the inmates to shoot.
'To re-conquer Ireland', says he, 'is my plan
With Macready and Co. and his bold Black and Tan.'

The town of Balbriggan they've burned to the ground
While bullets like hailstones were whizzing around;
And women left homeless by this evil clan.
They've waged war on the children, the bold Black and Tan.

From Dublin to Cork and from Thurles to Mayo
Lies a trail of destruction wherever they go;
With England to help and fierce passions to fan,
She must feel bloody proud of her bold Black and Tan.

Ah, then not by the terrors of England's foul horde,
For ne'er could a nation be ruled by the sword;
For our country we'll have yet in spite of her plan
Or ten times the number of bold Black and Tan.

We defeated Conscription in spite of their threats,
And we're going to defeat old Lloyd-George and his pets;
For Ireland and Freedom we're here to a man,
And we'll humble the pride of the bold Black and Tan.

Further battalions of regular troops, and a special force of ex-officers (even more highly paid than the Tans), were also brought in. The Volunteers and the I.R.B. began the systematic capture and destruction of barracks and the cutting of all lines of communication. The Republican communication lines were maintained largely by the women's organizations. The constabulary were cleared out of the villages and smaller towns. Prisoners went on hunger-strike. The Irish Labour Party and the T.U.C. called a token general strike; the prisoners were released; crowds demonstrating to welcome them were fired on. Railwaymen refused to operate trains carrying Black and Tans. Dockers refused to handle munitions. Coroner's juries repeatedly gave verdicts of *Murder* against the police. There was widespread land agitation, in the form of fence-breaking and cattle-driving.

The Dail, through the 'Sinn Fein courts', was building up an administration and a Republican police force. This was declared illegal. At the County Council and Rural District Council elections the Republicans again won a sweeping victory (including thirty-six out of the fifty-five Rural District Councils in Ulster). Daring raids were made on Government offices. Dublin, Cork and other cities were full of searchlights, barbed wire and tanks; houses were wrecked by day and night.

SEAN TREACY

(Killed in Dublin, 14th October, 1920)

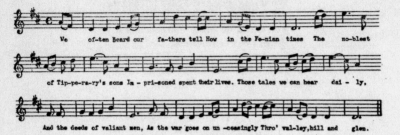

We often heard our fathers tell
How in the Fenian times
The noblest of Tipperary's sons
Imprisoned spent their lives.
Those tales we can hear daily,
And the deeds of valiant men,
As the war goes on unceasingly
Through valley, hill and glen.

They searched for Sean at midnight
His comrade with him slept.
Macready's murdering bloodhounds
In silence on them crept.
Our heroes fought as brave men should
And made a gallant fight;
With bullet food they did conclude
The lives of Smith and White.

In a crowded Dublin street Sean died
One cold October day;
The story will be told with pride
While men in Ireland stay,
With trusty gun held in his hand
Two sleuth hounds he laid low;
T'was well they knew this island through
They had no braver foe.

When the British saw the battle
They shook with fear and dread.
A machine-gun then did rattle
And our hero bold lay dead.
Sean Treacy killed! Sean Treacy killed!
Was borne along the breeze.
No bells were rung; no *caoin* was sung;
He died for Ireland free.

> While grass grows green in Ireland
> We'll think of you brave Sean!
> We'll sing your praise o'er hill and vale
> When grief and gloom are gone.
> And when the dawn of Freedom's sun
> Shines out in Irish skies,
> In our Gaelic tongue we'll tell our sons
> How brave Sean Treacy died.

Meanwhile, Lloyd George's Partition plan was going forward. The Home Rule Act was amended to exclude 'Ulster' (that is, out of Ulster's nine counties, the six now known as Northern Ireland—two of which had and have a large Republican majority). Organized anti-Catholic pogroms broke out in and around Belfast, as well as wanton and unlimited victimisation of every kind.

The R.I.C. grew demoralized; resignations began to pour in, and even mutiny occurred. Recruiting for the police force ceased altogether. Local magistrates resigned by hundreds. The Dail, however, continued its administrative and judicial work, when the British courts had collapsed.

General Macready's forty battalions did not suffice; he demanded nine more in order to establish martial law throughout Ireland. The practice of torturing prisoners to obtain information began. The co-operative creameries were systematically destroyed. Relatives of wanted but unfound men were shot in revenge. (It was now that the classic formula 'shot while attempting to escape' was coined.) An Act of Parliament gave even more extended powers and extraordinary immunities to the military, made refusal to inform punishable by six months imprisonment or £100 fine, and turned almost the whole population into offenders *ipso facto*. The entire nation was outlawed and the terror campaign indemnified in advance.

Coroner's inquests were abolished and replaced by secret military inquiries. Terence McSwiney, Lord Mayor of Cork in succession to McCurtain, was arrested, went on hunger-strike, was removed to England, continued the hunger-strike in Brixton, and died after seventy-two days without food. The day of his funeral (31st October, 1920) was held as a day of national mourning in Ireland.

TERENCE MCSWINEY

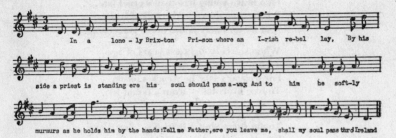

In a lonely Brixton Prison where an Irish rebel lay
By his side a priest is standing ere his soul should pass away
And to him he softly murmurs as he holds him by the hand:
Tell me Father ere you leave me shall my soul pass through Ireland?

Shall my soul pass through old Ireland, pass through Cork's fair city grand,
Shall I see the old cathedral where St. Patrick took his stand,
Shall I see the little chapel where I pledged my heart and hand,
Tell me this before you leave me, shall my soul pass through Ireland?

Tis for loving dear old Ireland in a prison cell I lie,
Tis for loving dear old Ireland in a foreign land I die.
Will you tell my little daughter, won't you make her understand—
Tell me father ere you leave me shall my soul pass through Ireland?

No part of Ireland was free from violence. Countless homes had been wrecked, and thousands were living in stables and barns. The executions went on. Notable in its effect was that of Kevin Barry, an eighteen-year-old student, the first Irish patriot to be hanged in Ireland since Robert Emmet 117 years before. His death precipitated scores of his fellow-students into the I.R.A.; he has become the national symbol of matryred youth. Here is one of the songs in his honour.

KEVIN BARRY

(Hanged in Dublin, 1st November, 1920)

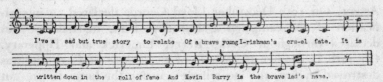

I've a sad but true story to relate
Of a brave young Irishman's cruel fate.
It is written down in the roll of fame
And Kevin Barry is the brave lad's name.

When scarcely eighteen years of age
To the Republican Army he was engaged
For Ireland's sake he struck a blow
To free his country from a tyrant foe.

In the fight with the foe against the crown
Young Barry shot a British soldier down,
He appeared and was tried by military
And sentenced to die on the gallows tree.

In the condemned cell awaiting his fate
He was asked to confess before it was too late:
Come tell us where your comrades may be
A pardon will be granted and we'll set you free.
Young Barry gazed with a look of scorn:
An Irish traitor never yet was born!
Carry out your sentence was the proud reply,
For Ireland I fought and for Ireland I'll die!

Outside the jail his comrades fell
On their knees in prayer to the prison bell
For to pray for the soul of a martyr friend
Who would rather die than to foemen bend.

Out from the jail then walked a priest
And the tears rolled down his manly cheeks;
Have they hung him, Father? his comrades cried.
—He's gone, but a braver lad never died.

The 'shooting by roster' policy of wholesale extermination resulted in the preventive reprisal known as Bloody Sunday, when fourteen British Intelligence agents were shot dead in their homes. Immediate counter-reprisals, the same day, included ten minutes' firing into a football crowd (twelve were killed, sixty wounded and hundreds injured) and the arrest and summary execution of three Dublin I.R.A. leaders. Granard and Tralee were sacked.

On 23rd November the 'Partition Bill' received the Royal Assent. On 10th December Lloyd George declared an intensification of the campaign against Sinn Fein. Martial law was declared throughout Cork, Kerry, Limerick and Tipperary. On 11th December the whole of the centre of Cork city was destroyed by fire, the incendiaries cutting the hoses to prevent the fire brigades from doing their job. The British Labour Commission, then on an investigation tour in Ireland, reported that the fires seemed 'an organized attempt to destroy the most valuable premises in the city'.

The death penalty was introduced for possessing arms or ammunition, wearing Volunteer uniform, and harbouring or aiding rebels. Four more counties were placed under martial law in January, 1921. The military governor of Cork ordered summary execution of those refusing information or aiding rebels. All such executions now met with instant reprisals, a death for a death. Seeking wounded men, the military raided the hospitals in defiance of the medical authorities; I.R.A. groups often snatched wounded men out of hospital just in time. General Crozier resigned his command, shocked by the brutality and indiscipline of the Black-and-Tans and even the regulars. General Gough described the situation as 'bloody and brutal anarchy'.

The new Government of Ireland Act came into force in May. Elections were held. In all Ireland the Republicans gained a majority of 140 to 44 (128 to 4 in the Twenty-six Counties and 12 to 40 in the Six Counties). The British Cabinet decided to reinforce the troops in Ireland to the utmost. Arrests and ambushes continued almost hourly. The Republican representatives rejected the Act and refused to meet except as Dail Eireann and in a free Republic. King George V opened the Stormont Parliament in Northern Ireland.

At last, on 25th June, Lloyd George wrote to De Valera (now back in Ireland 'on the run') proposing a conference with a view to peace. Irish delegates went to London, where they were formally offered the alternatives of accepting Partition (with a form of Dominion self-government for the Twenty-six Counties) or else 'immediate and terrible war' on a massive and all-out scale within three days.

The Irish delegation split. Some rejected Partition out of hand on any terms whatever, and absolutely refused to sign the Treaty. Others (notably Arthur Griffith and Michael Collins, who still had a price on his head of £1,000 dead or alive) fearing total obliteration and knowing their forces exhausted and their supplies meagre, agreed to sign. The latter formed a bare majority, and the Treaty became a fact. A Boundary Commission was set up to delimit Northern Ireland according to the wishes of the inhabitants of the Border areas. (It lapsed in 1925 and no report has ever been presented to Parliament.) British troops, police, auxiliaries and administrators were to be withdrawn from the Twenty-six Counties. So ended the Anglo-Irish War of 1918-21.

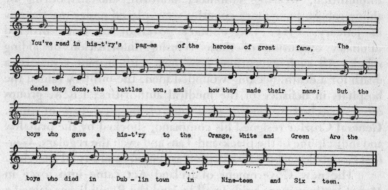

THE BOYS FROM THE COUNTY CORK

You've read in history's pages of the heroes of great fame,
The deeds they done, the battles won, and how they made their name;
But the boys who gave a history to the Orange White and Green
Are the boys who died in Dublin town in Nineteen and Sixteen.

Chorus:
Meet the boys from Kerry, meet the boys from Clare,
Dublin, Wicklow, Donegal, and the boys from Old Kildare;
Boys from the land beyond the seas, from Boston and New York,
But the boys that beat the Black and Tans were the boys from the County
Cork.

Cork gave us Mac Sweeney, a hero he did die,
Wicklow gave us Michael Dwyer in the days so long gone by,
Dublin gave us Padraic Pearse, MacBride and Cathal Brugh
And America gave us De Valera to lead old Ireland through.

Chorus

We seem to be divided, I really don't know why,
We've a glorious list of martyrs who for Ireland's cause did die;
Now why not get together and join in unity,
The North, the South, the East and West will set old Ireland free.

Chorus

'The Troubles' were far from ended, however. The split over the Treaty flared up almost at once into civil war between the Republicans (Sinn Feiners) and the Treatyites (Free Staters).

The cunning tyrant fooled them, when their fight was bravely won,
And he beat them at the table, when he failed to with the gun.
He tore their ranks asunder, with his greedy robber's hand,
And he tried divide and conquer as a cure for Ireland.

The Treaty (or Articles of Agreement) gave Northern Ireland the right (within one month) to opt for exclusion from the Irish Free State; provided for a Crown Representative comparable to the Governor-General of Canada; imposed an oath of allegiance to the Crown in virtue of 'common citizenship' and membership of the British Commonwealth; established Irish liability for a share of the National Debt of the United Kingdom; reserved the naval and coastal defence of Ireland to the Imperial forces (this meant British occupation of the ports of Berehaven, Cobh (Queenstown), Lough Swilly and Belfast Lough, known as the Treaty Ports); and limited the defence forces of the Free State.

This was obviously not a Treaty between two independent and equal States; equally obviously it was completely unacceptable to the Republican cause. Those Irish delegates who signed it had contravened their instructions from the Dail, which was bound to repudiate their action. The Republican Cabinet met on 8th December; Barton, Cosgrave, Collins and Griffith defended the Treaty; Brugha, De Valera and Stack opposed it; it was accepted on a four to three vote. De Valera, as President of the Republic, issued a Proclamation to the Irish people rejecting the Treaty. Griffith issued a counter-statement in favour of the Treaty, and fifteen members of the Catholic Hierarchy gave public support to it. The Council of the I.R.B. was divided (owing to the great influence of Collins). In the North, Lord Carson and Sir James Craig (later Lord Craigavon) made it clear that the Treaty conformed exactly to their wishes and proposals.

THE IRISH FREE STATE

I went to see David, to London to David, I went to see David, and what did he do? He gave me a Free State, a nice little Free State, A Free State that's tied up with Red, White and Blue.

I went to see David, to London to David,
I went to see David and what did he do?
He gave me a Free State, a nice little Free State,
A Free State that's tied up with Red, White and Blue.

I brought it to Dublin to show to Dail Eireann,
I brought it to Dublin and what did they do?
They asked me what kind of a thing was a Free State,
A Free State that's tied up with Red, White and Blue.

Three-quarters of Ireland a nation—I told them,
Tied on to the Empire with Red, White and Blue;
And an oath they must swear to King George and Queen Mary,
An oath they must swear to the son-in-law new.

I'm teaching them Irish and painting their boxes
All over with green, sure what more can I do?
Yet they tell me they want just an Irish Republic
Without any trimmings of Red, White and Blue!

On 6th January, 1922, De Valera offered his resignation from
the Presidency. The bitter debate in the Dail on 7th January
resulted in majorities of seven for the Treaty and of two against
De Valera's Presidency. Griffith formed an Executive, with
Collins, Cosgrave, Duffy, O'Higgins and Mulcahy as Ministers.
De Valera, with Brugha, Stack and all their supporters, left the
Dail. The I.R.A. (now the official army of the Republic) split
over its allegiance to the Dail, whose authority was in doubt. The
evacuation of British troops and police began. So did Anti-Treaty
resignations and desertions from the Irish Army. De Valera and
the anti-Treaty deputies formed the Cumann-na-Poblachta
(Republican Party) and issued a journal, *An Poblacht na h-Eireann*
(The Republic of Ireland), in which Erskine Childers took the
lead. The women's organization, Cumann na-mBan, rejected the
Treaty by a vote of 419 to 63, elected Constance Markiewicz
President, and called on pro-Treaty members to resign.

Northern Ireland 'specials' began raids and skirmishes on the
Free State side of the border, and on 11th February the first
shots in the Irish Civil War were fired at Clones in County
Monaghan. Pogroms occured in Belfast, where, for example, a
bomb was thrown among Catholic children playing in the street,
killing three of them.

Now don't play ball in Belfast Town
For a big bomb will blow you to Kingdom Come.
Think of the chislers, one, two, three,
Down comes a big bomb, that's the end of me!

The Irish Army demanded a Convention; only anti-Treaty men attended (220 delegates representing 49 Brigades). The Convention reaffirmed allegiance to the Republic and elected an Executive to draft a new Army Constitution. (Henceforward the anti-Treaty Volunteers reserved the title I.R.A. for themselves and referred to the pro-Treaty forces as the Free State Army; the latter however continued to call themselves the Irish Republican Army and their opponents simply mutineers.)

The anti-Treaty Army Convention met again on 9th April and elected an Executive of sixteen—which included Liam Lynch, Liam Mellowes (Connolly's successor), Rory O'Connor, Earnan O'Malley and Peadar O'Donnell—as well as an Army Council, with Lynch as Chief of Staff and Mellowes as Quartermaster General. They at once took over several barracks from pro-Treaty forces, many of whom offered no resistance. On 13th April the Dublin Brigade occupied the Four Courts, in order to set up Military Headquarters. Meanwhile raids were made on post offices and branches of the Bank of Ireland to obtain money; stores and transport were commandeered; recruiting to pro-Treaty forces was obstructed; a boycott on trade with Belfast was operated; and communications were cut to hamper pro-Treaty meetings. The British authorities handed over considerable quantities of arms and equipment to the Free State Forces.

Collins and De Valera made a Coalition Pact, which was denounced by Winston Churchill and Griffith. General Macready prepared to shell Dublin and blockade Cork and Limerick. Collins repudiated the Pact.

In June the Catholic Hospital in Belfast was attacked by an armed mob. Thousands of Catholic fugitives fled from Northern Ireland to Dublin and to Glasgow. Border raids increased. The I.R.A. headquarters in Dublin split on the question of making war on British troops still in the Twenty-six Counties and on the Northern Ireland forces; Brugha and Lynch and a small majority opposed the proposal; the minority in favour of it entrenched themselves in the Four Courts, under McKelvey, Mellowes, O'Connor and O'Malley.

The shooting of Sir Henry Wilson in London on 22nd June precipitated a crisis. Lloyd George ordered Collins to take action against the Four Courts men (although they had expressly repudiated the killing of Wilson), and promised military

assistance. On 28th June heavy artillery opened fire on the Four
Courts.

> They shelled their own upon that day
> With English guns and cannon,
> 'We're free at last from British rule.'
> Wolfe Tone weeps in Dungannon!
>
> Sure God won't pardon cowards all
> Who signed that British paper
> And we shall fight till Ireland's free
> From England and Free Stater!

Lynch and the Dublin Brigade issued a proclamation (over
their own names and those of the Four Courts men) on behalf of
the Irish Republican Army; hotels were seized for Republican
headquarters; Cumann-na-mBan were mobilised. The civil war
had started in grim earnest.

The shelling went on for three days; at last the Four Courts
went up in flames. McKelvey, Mellowes and O'Connor were
taken prisoner. The hotel headquarters of the Dublin Brigade
were shelled; De Valera and others escaped, on Brugha's orders;
Brugha himself remained to the last, and was shot down on 5th
July as he left the burning building, still refusing to surrender.

All Ireland was fighting. In Britain, Churchill and Birkenhead
sounded a note of triumph. The Free State Government created a
War Council under Collins, and refused to summon the Dail.
The Republicans controlled the whole of Munster, and much of
the rest of the country, but the Free State forces were in-
comparably better armed. The I.R.A. retreated from town after
town, operating a 'scorched earth' policy.

Griffith died on 12th August. Ten days later Collins was
killed in action, in an I.R.A. ambush in County Cork. Lynch
and other army leaders refused consultations with De Valera.
The Free State Assembly elected Cosgrave President, authorized
arrest and detention without investigation, charge or trial, and
applied the death penalty to minor offences.

On 11th November Erskine Childers was captured; he was
tried in camera and executed on 24th November. McKelvey,
Mellowes and O'Connor were executed on 8th December. (In
all seventy-seven Republicans were executed by the Free State
authorities between November, 1922, and May, 1923.) Govern-

ment property was destroyed in reprisal against the executions. Running fights lasting days at a time went on all over Ireland.

The Free State Army had inexhaustible supplies of war material from England, while the Republican Army was growing exhausted. The people were increasingly weary and anxious for peace; the Republican forces had as many men in the hands of the enemy as in action, and they sustained very severe losses at Aherlow and in Connemara and Kerry. The I.R.A. prisoners were notoriously ill-treated by the Free State forces; the prisons were overcrowded, with many women and girls, and with many deportees from Britain. Shocking anti-Republican reprisals occurred in Kerry.

The Republicans began to seek a way out, short of surrender. The I.R.A. executive rejected a peace resolution by one vote. Lynch was killed in action. Stack was captured. The executive met again; appointed General Aiken (of a neutral section of the armed forces) as Chief of Staff, and empowered him to offer negotiation.

On 27th April De Valera and Aiken issued a Cease Fire proclamation, based on the principles of the inalienable sovereign rights of the Irish nation; the exclusive derivation of governmental authority from the Irish people; the ultimate right of appeal to the people by majority vote; the refusal of victimization; the freedom of speech, assembly and the Press; and the subordination of the military forces to the National Assembly.

The fighting ceased on 30th April, 1923.

WRAP THE GREEN FLAG ROUND ME, BOYS

Wrap the green flag round me, boys,
To die were far more sweet
With Ireland's noble emblem, boys,
To be my winding sheet.

In life I loved to see it wave,
And follow where it led,
But now my eyes grow dim—my hand
Would grasp its last bright shred.

Chorus:
   Then wrap the green flag round me, boys,
   To die were far more sweet
   With Ireland's noble emblem, boys,
   To be my winding sheet.

And I had hoped to meet you, boys,
On many a well-fought field,
When to our sacred banner, boys,
The traitorous foe would yield.
But now, alas! I am denied
My dearest earthly prayer,
You'll follow and you'll meet the foe,
But I shall not be there.

Chorus

But though my body moulders, boys,
My spirit shall be free
And every comrade's honour, boys,
Will yet be dear to me.
And in the thick and bloody fight
Let not your courage lag,
For I'll be there and hovering near
Around the dear old flag.

Chorus

                                        J. K. O' Reilly

Since that time, Ireland has remained partitioned, and the Twenty-six Counties (called the Irish Free State till 1938, then Eire till 1949, and now the Republic of Ireland) has continued the struggle on a political plane. De Valera formed a new political party, *Fianna Fail* (Soldiers of Destiny), in opposition to the Free State party *Fine Gael*. His policy has remained implacably anti-Partition, and the 1938 Irish Constitution (De Valera was Prime Minister from 1932 till after World War II) expressly claims the whole territory of Ireland as its field *de jure* though not *de facto*. The 'elevation of six counties to the rank and status of a nation' was confirmed and perpetuated by Britain in an Act of Parliament in 1950.

A section of the 1923 I.R.A., however, did not accept the Cease Fire order; they refused to lay down their arms, rejected the authority of the Assembly, and remain to this day in opposition. To this section the war of liberation still continues.

> Take it down from the mast, Irish traitors,
> Tis the flag we Republicans claim.
> It can never be owned by Free Staters
> Who shed nothing on it but shame.
> Then leave it to those who are willing,
> To uphold it in war or in peace,
> Those men who intend to do killing
> Until England's tyranny cease.

The Sinn Fein party has recently re-emerged. This booklet, however, is not the place for an examination of current Irish politics. Suffice it to say that the question of the Border is a major issue for all parties and groupings, both right and left, both in the north and in the south. 'Ireland one, and Ireland free—is not this the definition of Ireland a nation?' said Patrick Pearse.

IV

SOME OTHER IRISH SONGS

IT MAY PERHAPS BE WONDERED WHY SUCH SONGS AS *The Mountains of Mourne*, and above all the *Irish Melodies* of Thomas Moore (which include such world-famous platform songs as *The Last Rose of Summer*) have not been mentioned here. There are good reasons.

Moore has been described as 'a champion cushion-fighter for Ireland'. As he himself admitted in a moment of insight, in the song so aptly and wistfully entitled *O Blame Not The Bard*, what he did was to offer his country's oppressors an inoffensive and genteel portrayal of her sufferings, to the end that '*thy masters themselves, as they rivet thy chains, Shall pause at the song of their captive and weep*!'—without, of course, making any move to unrivet the chains.

Moore's *Melodies* do not truly represent either Ireland's characteristic music or Ireland's proud, stubborn, heroic spirit. His enchanting airs, his seductive verbal harmonies, seem more English than Irish. Hazlitt said shrewdly that Moore had 'converted the wild harp of Erin into a musical snuff-box', and the great Irish song-collector, Sparling, declared that Moore had 'tinkered most of the old tunes he used into drawing-room shapes'.

Drawing-room is the word. Moore, who proudly and complacently used to count the tears on the cheeks of duchesses as they listened to him, appeals most to those who are willing to sentimentalize over a country's woes while deploring or opposing any active attempt to remedy them. He himself, in one of his prefaces, writes: '. . . . there is no-one who deprecates more sincerely than I do any appeal to the passions of an ignorant and angry multitude . . . a work of this nature . . . looks much higher . . . it is found upon the pianofortes of the rich and educated'.

In another of his prefaces Moore wrote: 'Ballads have long since lost their revolutionary power'. He did not expect a Thomas Davis to emerge. It was of Davis, not Moore, that *The Times* said 'his songs are far more dangerous than O'Connell's speeches'.

Consider the times in which Moore lived, 1779-1852. At the time of the Great Rebellion he was a young man of nineteen—like his fellow-student Robert Emmet. He lived through the times of the Tithe War, the minor famines of the 1820's, the emancipation movement, the Repeal Agitation, the Young Ireland movement, the great Famine, the 1848 Insurrection and the beginnings of Tenants Right agitation. This was no period of quiescent resignation or of plaintive lamentations, but a time of great events, massive movements, stirring deeds and heroic men. Moore was contemporary with Tone, Emmet, McCracken, O'Connell, O'Connor, Davis, Lalor, Duffy, Mitchel. Yet he cries 'vanished for ever that fair sunny vision', and can actually claim the Duke of Wellington—of all people!—as Ireland's redeeming genius, 'Star of the Isle' and 'rainbow of hope'.

Outside Ireland were such figures as Paine, Blake, Owen, Shelley, Byron, Cobbett, Dickens and innumerable other fighters for the rights of man. In England these were the days of the Industrial Revolution, bread riots, mutinies, Owen's socialistic experiments, the violent repressive measures called the Six Acts, the March of the Blanketeers and the Peterloo massacre, the Luddite machine breaking riots, the Reform Bill agitation, the Poor Law agitation, the Chartist movement, the battle over the Factory Acts, and the steady growth of trade union organization in spite of imprisonment and transportation.

In Europe this period saw the Great French Revolution of 1789, the Revolutionary and Napoleonic Wars of 1794-1815, the French Revolution of 1830 and the Year of Revolutions in almost every country in Europe in 1848. It was indeed quite unmistakably a time of enormous conflict, 'prolonged struggles transforming circumstances and men'.

But to Moore all was pervaded with a sweet and tender melancholy, resolved into a gentle sigh for the distant and troubled past now safely dead. His entrancingly seductive songs serve as a figleaf to hide the naked reality of violent struggle.

And yet many of his airs are exquisite and utterly memorable. *She Is Far From The Land*, *The Harp That Once Through Tara's Halls*, *There Is Not In The Wide World A Valley So Sweet*, *Oft In The Stilly Night*, and many many others, are beautiful indeed. And in their proper place, the drawing-room or intimate music-room, they are delightful show-pieces. They are not, however, typical of Irish song; they represent a 'posying-up' of the bitter facts, welcome to those whose interest it is to keep those facts unchanged.

Moore was an exceedingly successful as well as very popular man. He amassed a fortune from his songs and poems. Naturally enough, there has been since his day (and still is) a whole school of songs of similar type. Such are *Galway Bay*, *The Hills of Donegal*, *The Mountains of Mourne*, and other such sentimental glosses.

Also (particularly, though not only, in America), in course of time the exile and transportation songs degenerated and were commercialized into maudlin emotionalism like that of *Mother McCree*, *A Little Bit of Heaven*, *Did Your Mother Come From Ireland*, and so forth; national ballads were emasculated; the tough jocularity of Irish comic songs was diminished into the 'aren't they sweet' style.

All of these, and their kin, are not so much Irish as 'Oirish'. That is, they are fakes or partial fakes which trade, very profitably, on the nostalgia of the displaced Irish themselves and on the ignorant sympathy or pity or curiosity of the non-Irish, without the slightest interest in the real problems of Ireland today or at any other time.

Many such 'Oirish' songs are positively anti-Irish. Such are the songs which foster the legend (always applied to all colonized peoples and subject races) that the Irish are (a) funny; (b) quaint; (c) quarrelsome; (d) charmingly irresponsible; (e) stupidly dangerous. Subscribing to this legend, to however small an extent, betrays bias against the Irish people and their legitimate aspirations.

For instance, *Hot Asphalte* gives a revolting picture of Irish labourers casually committing a particularly barbarous and wanton murder on the merest shred of provocation and with callous jocularity. It is, presumably, supposed to be taken as demonstrating an understandable dislike of policemen; but it is in fact a very unpleasant example of the 'dangerous and irresponsible' legend.

Similarly, *No Irish Need Apply* helps to foster the 'stupid and violent' legend. The Irish labourer who cannot find work solves the problem by upping with his 'shillelagh' and bashing the boss on the head. Another of the same kind is *The Day that Pat Came Out On Shtrike* (sic): the boss gives the workers more than they ask on seeing the 'shillelagh'. On the surface it might appear that songs of this sort mean to applaud the Irishman's courage; but since this 'courage' is frequently misapplied, and seldom is any gleam of intelligence seen in 'Paddy's' eye, the compliment is a squinting one.

The shillelagh-swinging, fight-you-for-nothing, Murdher-and-Bejabers 'Pat' or 'Paddy' does not exist and never did. This mythical moron should be done away with by the use of that Irish-invented weapon, the boycott.

The true songs of Ireland are a very different matter. Enough has been quoted above to show the quality and temper of the more strictly political songs. There is also a great body of song of a more generalized character, falling roughly into the following categories: laments for the lost or the dead; songs of exile and transportation; narrative songs; jocular songs.

Work-songs in the English language are very rare, though there are plenty in Gaelic. This represents a form of passive resistance to exploitation: the Irish were not prepared to make songs about work done for the benefit of the conqueror.

As for love-songs, it is hard to establish a separate category. There are scarcely any (except, typically enough, in Moore's *Melodies*) of the type of *Drink To Me Only* or *Cherry Ripe*. Most of the Irish love-songs are laments, like *Shule Aroon*, *The Flower of Finae*, *Philemy Hieland*. Some of the love songs are simple narrative, like *Young Mollie Ban* or *Lovely Willie*; some few are jocular, like *Brian Og and Molly Bawn*. It is, however, characteristic of

Ireland that the great majority of the love-songs are full of historical and social allusions, and that many of them overlap the categories altogether. *Henry Joy McCracken*, for example, is a street-corner ballad which is also a narrative love-song and a lament for the dead and a political song of '98.

An important linguistic point is the frequent use of symbolic 'code names' for Ireland. There were very practical reasons for this during the Penal days; later it became fixed as a poetic tradition. Ireland has probably more names than any other country on earth. As well as Ireland or Erin, she is *Inisfail* (Island of Destiny) or *Inishfallen; Kathleen Na Houlihan; Countess Cathleen; Grania* or *Granuaile; Nora Criona; The Shan Van Vocht* (Little Old Woman); *The Woman of the Roads; The Silk of the Kine; The Snowy-Breasted Pearl; Roisin Dhu* (Dark Rosebud) or *The Little Black Rose* or *Dark Rosaleen;* and many more.

By the use of this device of a metaphorical name, many rebel songs were disguised as love-songs or pathetic ditties. One of the finest examples of an apparent love-song which is really a rallying-cry is *Dark Rosaleen*, by James Clarence Mangan (of *The Nation*), which—presumably as a love-song—is included in the *Oxford Book of English Verse*. (It is a very free rendering of the Gaelic song *Roisin Dhu*.)

> O the Erne shall run red
>   With redundance of blood
> The earth shall rock beneath our tread
>   And flames wrap hill and wood,
> And gun-peal and slogan-cry
>   Wake many a glen serene,
> Ere you shall fade, ere you shall die,
>   My Dark Rosaleen!
>   My own Rosaleen!
> The Judgement Hour must first be nigh,
> Ere you can fade, ere you can die,
>   My Dark Rosaleen!

'You have vowed to win the freedom of your country, and you must wail no more,' said Thomas Francis Meagher in 1847. *You must wail no more.* The great Irish wail has resounded throughout the world; but it is time the Irish looked once more toward the future and showed themselves the true heirs of the United Irishmen, the Young Irelanders, the Fenians and the Citizen Army.

'. . . let us take forth, and go forward in our learning.'
What has happened to Ireland's ballad tradition? Why have the
last thirty years been almost barren of outstanding songs?

One of the reasons is the fact that Ireland did win a partial
and hamstrung victory. There *is* a sovereign independent Irish
Republic. Its jurisdiction, however, does not extend over the
whole of the national territory. Ireland is partitioned. Moreover,
the existence of the Republic has not significantly improved the
conditions of the common people; cheap labour remains the
principal export, and the emigration figures have risen by
40 per cent in thirty years.

The result of this ambiguous situation has been, as far as
songs and ballads are concerned, either a half-hearted reiteration
of the most threadbare and ineffectual of the old themes (and
increasingly depressed renderings of the old songs), or else
snatches of confusion and disunity as regards the present and the
future. There are one or two sarcastic parodies, which leave a
bitter aftertaste, such as 'Three-quarters of a Nation Once
Again', or 'God Save the Twenty-six Counties, Said They
Proudly'; there are one or two inconclusive attempts at criticis-
ing the Irish Government, such as 'To believe that, how green
must we be'.

The only potential makers of forceful and memorable
ballads are those who have a positive progressive vision of
Ireland's future. Such songs have not yet appeared; this is
partly because progressive people have themselves, unthinkingly,
been carrying on the *Poor Old Granuaile* tradition, and partly
because they have been (sometimes, it must be admitted,
deliberately) neglecting and even belittling culture.

Yet the ballad-makers of Ireland are not an extinct race.
There can and will be genuine and moving ballads of today and
tomorrow, provided the vision of the possible future is so
presented as to stir the imagination and arouse the confidence of
the common people. There are themes in plenty—the 'bog of
covetousness' in which many of the liberators have stuck; the
'thicket of bramble-bush words' in which they lose themselves
and the people; the fact that masses of Irishmen and Irishwomen
'can hardly get bread but with great difficulty'; the facts that
after thirty years of independent sovereignty the Irish Republic's
principal and increasing export is still unemployed workers, and
that her marriage age is the highest in the whole world. All these,

and many others of more local purport, are subjects for ballads as movingly effective as any that have gone before.

Confusion and apathy can be done away with only by knowledge and inspiration. To the making of good songs, inspiration in particular is essential. Inspiration comes from vision, the vision of what could and should and shall be. Vision produced the best of Ireland's national songs—the vision of a free, independent and prosperous Ireland. Today should dawn again the vision of an Ireland not merely free from English oppression, but free from *all* oppression within her own shores.

If that spark is once struck into the minds of the people, it will kindle the 'living blaze that nothing shall withstand'. Such a blaze without its songs and ballads cannot even be imagined by the Irish. First, however, there must be the imagination to see and to present the vision.

A cynic once said that 'Ireland's future is her past'. This may well seem true so long as Ireland sits drowning in the seas of her own tears. Let her not be overwhelmed by the mournful grandeur of her keening, but say with Henry Joy: *My love, be cheerful, for tears and fears are vain.* Let her build on the magnificent boldness and sweeping inspiration of what is positive in her proud national tradition. Ireland's future is *now*.

SUPPLEMENT

GOD SAVE IRELAND
Air: Tramp, tramp, tramp
(*The prayer of the Manchester Martyrs, 1867*)

High upon the gallows tree swung the noble-hearted three,
By the vengeful tyrant stricken in their bloom;
But they met him face to face, with the courage of their race,
And they went with souls undaunted to their doom.

> *Chorus:*
> 'God save Ireland!' said the heroes;
> 'God save Ireland!' said they all.
> 'Whether on the scaffold high
> Or the battlefield we die,
> O, what matter when for Ireland dear we fall!'

Girt around with cruel foes, still their courage proudly rose,
For they thought of hearts that loved them far and near;
Of the millions true and brave o'er the ocean's swelling wave,
And the friends in holy Ireland ever dear.

Chorus

Climbed they up the rugged stair, rang their voices out in prayer,
Then with England's fatal cord around them cast,
Close beside the gallows tree kissed like brothers lovingly
True to home and faith and freedom to the last.

Chorus

Never till the latest day shall the memory pass away
Of the gallant lives thus given for our land;
But on the cause must go, amid joy or weal or woe,
Till we make this Isle a Nation free and grand.

Chorus   *T. D. Sullivan*

THE WEARING OF THE GREEN
(Old Version, 1798)

I met with Napper Tandy,
And he took me by the hand,
Saying how is old Ireland?
And how does she stand?
She's the most distressful country
That ever yet was seen;
They are hanging men and women
For wearing of the green!
  O Wearing of the green,
  O Wearing of the green,
  My native land, I cannot stand,
  For wearing of the green.

My father loved you tenderly,
He lies within your breast;
While I, that would have died for you,
Must never so be blest:
For laws, their cruel laws, have said
That seas should roll between
Old Ireland and her faithful sons
Who love to wear the green.
  O Wearing of the green,
  O Wearing of the green,
  My native land I cannot stand,
  For wearing of the green.

I care not for the Thistle,
And I care not for the Rose;
When bleak winds round us whistle,
Neither down nor crimson shows.

But like hope to him that's friendless,
When no joy around is seen,
O'er our graves with love that's endless
Blooms our own immortal green.
    O Wearing of the green,
    O Wearing of the green,
    My native land, I cannot stand,
    For wearing of the green.

THE PATRIOT MOTHER

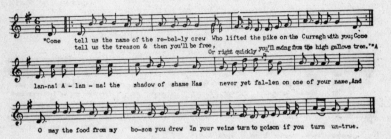

'Come tell us the name of the rebelly crew,
Who lifted the pike on the Curragh with you;
Come tell us the treason and then you'll be free,
Or right quickly you'll swing from the high gallows **tree.**'

'*Alanna! Alanna!* the shadow of shame
Has never yet fallen on one of your name,
And O may the food from my bosom you drew,
In your veins turn to poison, if *you* turn untrue.

'The foul words—O let them not blacken your tongue,
That would prove to your friends and your country **a wrong,**
Or the curse of a mother, so bitter and dread,
With the wrath of the Lord—may they fall on your **head!**

'I have no one but you in the whole world wide,
Yet false to your pledge, you's ne'er stand at my side:
If a traitor you lived, you'd be farther away
From my heart than, if true, you were wrapped in **the clay.**

'O deeper and darker the mourning would be,
For your falsehood so base, than your death proud and **free,**
Dearer, far fearer than ever to me,
My darling, you'll be on the brave gallows tree!

'Tis holy, *agra*, from the bravest and best—
Go! go! from my heart, and be joined with the rest,
Alanna machree! O alanna machree!*
Sure a "stag" and a traitor you never would be.'

There's no look of a traitor upon the young brow
That's raised to the tempters so haughtily now;
No traitor e'er held up the firm head so high—
No traitor e'er show'd such a proud flashing eye.

On the high gallows tree! on the brave gallows tree!
Where smiled leaves and blossoms, his sad doom met he!
But it never bore blossom so pure or so fair
As the heart of the martyr that hangs from it there.

*O child of my heart.

Mary Eva Kelly
(Eva of *The Nation*)

THE BLARISMOOR TRAGEDY
(17th May, 1797)

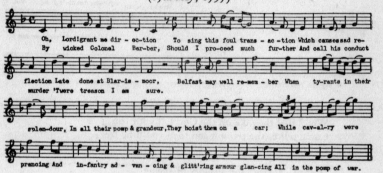

Oh, Lord! grant me direction,
To sing this foul transaction
Which causes sad reflection
Late done at Blarismoor,
By wicked Colonel Barber,
Should I proceed much further
And call his conduct murder
'Twere treason I am sure.

Belfast may well remember
When tyrants in their splendour,
In all their pomp and grandeur,
They hoist them on a car;
While cavalry were prancing
And infantry advancing
And glittering armour glancing
All in the pomp of war.

They were of good behaviour,
No heroes e'er were braver,
But a perjured base deceiver
He swore their lives away;

For the sake of golden store
This villain falsely swore,
And the crime we now deplore
In sorrow and dismay.

Amidst a hollow square
Well guarded front and rear,
With guns and bayonets there
Their constancy to move—
When they received their sentence
Their hearts felt no relentings
They bowed to each acquaintance
And kneeled to God above.

Their foes held consultation
To find our combination,
And then this exhortation
Curs'd Barber did propose—
'Arise from your devotion,
Take pardon and promotion,
Or death will be your portion
Unless you now disclose.'

Some moments then they mused,
For their senses were confused
But, smiling, they refused
And made him this reply—
'We own we are United,
Of death we're not affrighted,
And hope to be requited
By Him who rules on high.'

The guns were then presented,
The balls their bosoms entered,
While multitudes lamented
The shocking sight to see.
Those youthful martyrs four
Lay weltering in their gore,
And the plain besprinkled o'er
With the blood of liberty.

In coffins they were hurried,
From Blarismoor were carried,
And hastily were buried,
While thousands sank with grief,
Crying, 'Grania, we much wonder
You rise not from your slumber,
With voice as loud as thunder
To grant us some relief!'

TIPPERARY RECRUITING SONG
(Also sung to the air of *The Peeler and the Goat*.)

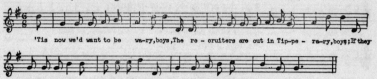

'Tis now we'd want to be wa-ry, boys, The re-cruiters are out in Tip-pe-ra-ry, boys; If they offer a glass, we'll wink as they pass—We're old birds for chaff in Tippe-ra-ry, boys.

'Tis now we'd want to be wary, boys,
The recruiters are out in Tipperary, boys;
If they offer a glass, we'll wink as they pass—
We're old birds for chaff in Tipperary, boys.

Then, hurrah for the gallant Tipperary boys
Although we're 'cross and contrary' boys;
There's never a one will handle a gun,
Except for the Green and Tipperary, boys.

Now mind what John Bull did here, my boys,
In the days of our Famine and fear, my boys;
He burned and sacked, he plundered and racked,
Old Ireland of Irish to clear, my boys.

Now Bull wants to pillage and rob, my boys,
And put the proceeds in his fob, my boys;
But let each Irish blade just stick to his trade,
And let Bull do his own dirty job, my boys.

So never to 'list be in haste, my boys,
Or a glass of drugged whisky to taste, my boys;
If to India you go, it's to grief and to woe,
And to rot and to die like a beast, my boys.

But now he is beat for men, my boys,
His army is getting so thin, my boys,
With the fever and ague, the sword and the plague,
O the devil a fear that he'll win, my boys.

Then mind not the nobblin' old schemer, boys,
Though he says that he's richer than Damer, boys;
Though he bully and roar, his power is o'er ,
And his black heart will shortly be tamer, boys.

Now, isn't Bull peaceful and civil, boys,
In his mortal distress and his evil, boys?
But we'll cock each *caubeen* when his sergeants are seen,
And we'll tell them to go to the devil, boys.

Then hurrah for the gallant Tipperary boys!
Although 'we're cross and contrary', boys
There's never a one will handle a gun,
Except for the Green and Tipperary, boys.

THE CORK MEN AND NEW YORK MEN

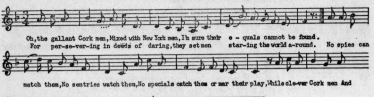

Oh, the gallant Cork men,
Mixed with New York men,
I'm sure their equals cannot be found;
For persevering, in deeds of daring,
They set men staring the world around.
No spies can match them,
No sentries watch them,
No specials catch them or mar their play,
While the clever Cork men
And cute New York men
Work new surprises by night and day.

Sedate and steady,
Calm, quick and ready,
They boldly enter, but make no din,
Where'er such trifles, as Snider rifles,
And bright six-shooters are stored within.
The Queen's round towers,
Can't baulk their powers,
Off go the weapons by sea and shore,
To where the Cork men
And smart New York men
Are daily piling their precious store.

John Bull, in wonder,
With voice like thunder,
Declares such plunder he must dislike;
They next may roll in, and sack Haulbowline,
Or, on a sudden, run off with Spike*.
His peace has vanished,
His joys are banished,
And gay or happy no more he'll be,
Until those Cork men
And wild New York men
Are sunk together beneath the sea.

Oh, bold New York men
And daring Cork men,
We own your pleasures should all grow dim,
On thus discerning, and plainly learning
That your amusement gives pain to *him*.
Yet from this nation,
This salutation,
Leaps forth, and echoes with thunderous sound—
'Here's to all Cork men,
Likewise New York men,
Who stand for Ireland the world around!'

*Spike Island.   *T. D. Sullivan*

FOLLOW ME UP TO CARLOW

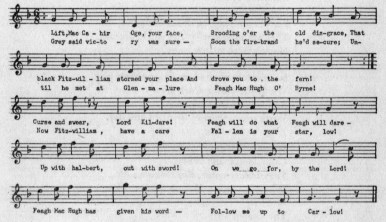

Lift, Mac Cahir Oge, your face,
Brooding o'er the old disgrace,
That black Fitzwilliam stormed your place
And drove you to the fern!
Grey said victory was sure—
Soon the Firebrand he'd secure;
Until he met at Glenmalure,
Feagh Mac Hugh O'Byrne!

> *Chorus:*
> Curse and swear, Lord Kildare!
> Feagh will do what Feagh will dare—
> Now, Fitzwilliam, have a care—
> Fallen is your star, low!
> Up with halbert, out with sword!
> On we go; for by the Lord!
> Feagh Mac Hugh has given his word—
> Follow me up to Carlow!

See the swords of Glen Imayle
Flashing o'er the English Pale!
See all the children of the Gael
Beneath O'Byrne's banners!
Rooster of a fighting stock,
Would you let a Saxon cock
Crow out upon an Irish rock?
Fly up and teach him manners!

Chorus

From Tassagart to Clonmore,
Flows a stream of Saxon gore!
Och, great is Rory Oge O'More
At sending loons to Hades!
White is sick and Lane is fled!
Now for black Fitzwilliam's head—
We'll send it over dripping red
To Liza and her ladies!

Chorus   *P. J. McCall*

It is said that this air was first performed by the pipers of
Feagh MacHugh as he marched to attack Carlow after his victory
over Lord Deputy Grey at Glenmalure (1580).

GREEN UPON THE CAPE
(*A Northern variant of 'The Wearing of the Green'*)

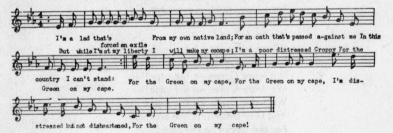

I'm a lad that's forced an exile
From my own native land;
For an oath that's passed against me
In this country I can't stand:
But while I'm at my liberty
I will make my escape;
I'm a poor distressed Croppy
For the Green on my cape!
For the Green on my cape!
For the Green on my cape!
I'm distressed, but not disheartened,
For the Green on my cape!

But I'll go down to Belfast,
To see that seaport gay,
And tell my aged parents
In this country I can't stay:
O 'tis dark will be their sorrow,
But no truer hearts I've seen;
And they'd rather see me dying
Than a traitor to the Green!
O the wearing of the Green!
O the wearing of the Green!
May the curse of Cromwell darken
Each traitor to the Green!

When I went down to Belfast,
And saw that seaport grand,
My aged parents blessed me,
And blessed poor Ireland,
Then I went unto a captain,
And bargained with him cheap;
He told me that his whole ship's crew
Wore Green on the cape!
O the Green on the cape!
O the Green on the cape!
God's blessing guard the noble boys
With Green on the cape!

'Twas early the next morning
Our gallant ship set sail;
Kind Heaven did protect her
With a pleasant Irish gale,
We landed safe in Paris,
Where victualling was cheap—
They knew we were United,
We wore Green on the cape!
We wore Green on the cape!
We wore Green on the cape!
And they treated us like brothers
For the Green on the cape!

'Take courage now, my brave boys,
For here you have good friends,
And we'll send a convoy with you,
Down by their Orange dens;
And if they should oppose us,
With our weapons sharp and keen
We'll make them rue and curse the day
That e'er they saw the Green!
That e'er they saw the Green!
That e'er they saw the Green!
We'll show them our authority
For wearing of the Green!'

O may the wind of Freedom
Soon send young Boney o'er,
And we'll plant the Tree of Liberty
Upon our Shamrock shore;
O we'll plant it with our weapons,
While the English tyrants gape
To see their bloody flag torn down
To Green on the cape!
O the wearing of the Green!
O the wearing of the Green!
God grant us soon to see that day,
And freely wear the Green!

THE FAIR OF TURLOUGHMORE

Come tell me, dearest mother, what makes my father stay
Or what can be the reason that he's been so long away?
Oh hold your tongue, my darling son, your tears do grieve me sore,
I fear he has been murdered at the fair of Turloughmore.

Come all you tender Christians I hope you will draw near
It's of this dreadful murder I mean to let you hear:
Concerning those poor people whose loss we do deplore
(The Lord have mercy on their souls) they died at Turloughmore.

'Twas on the first of August the truth I will declare
Those people they assembled that day all at the fair;
But little was their notion what evil was in store
All by the bloody Peelers at the fair of Turloughmore.

Were you to see that dreadful sight 'twould grieve your heart I know
To see those lovely women and the men all lying low;
God help their tender parents, they will never see them more,
For cruel was their murder at the fair of Turloughmore.

It's for that base bloodthirsty crew remark the word I say
The Lord he will reward them against the Judgement Day,
The blood they've taken innocent for it they'll suffer sore,
And the treatment that they gave to us that day at Turloughmore.

The morning of their trial as they stood in the dock,
The words they spoke were feeling, the people round them flock,
'I tell you Judge and Jury, the truth I will declare
It was Brew that ordered us to fire, that evening at the fair.'

Now to conclude and finish this sad and doleful lay
I hope their souls are happy against the Judgement Day,
It was little time they got, we know, when they fell like new-mown hay,
May the Lord have mercy on their souls against the Judgement Day.

DUNLAVIN GREEN

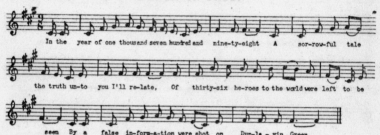

In the year of one thousand seven hundred and ninety eight
A sorrowful tale the truth unto you I'll relate
Of thirty-six heroes to the world were left to be seen
By a false information were shot on Dunlavin Green.

Bad luck to you, Saunders, for you did their lives betray;
You said a parade would be held on that very day,
Our drums they did rattle—our fifes they did sweetly play;
Surrounded we were and privately marched away.

Quite easy they led us as prisoners through the town,
To be slaughtered on the plain, we then were forced to kneel down,
Such grief and such sorrow were never before there seen,
When the blood ran in streams down the dykes of Dunlavin Green.

There is young Matty Farrell, has plenty of cause to complain,
Also the two Duffys, who were shot down on the plain,
And young Andy Ryan, his mother distracted will run
For her own brave boy, her beloved eldest son.

Bad luck to you, Saunders, bad luck may you never shun!
That the widow's curse may melt you like snow in the sun,
The cries of the orphans whose murmurs you cannot screen,
For the murder of their dear fathers, on Dunlavin Green.

Some of our boys to the hills they are going away,
Some of them are shot, and some of them going to sea,
Micky Dwyer in the mountains to Saunders he owes a spleen,
For his loyal brothers, who were shot on Dunlavin Green.

MICHAEL DWYER

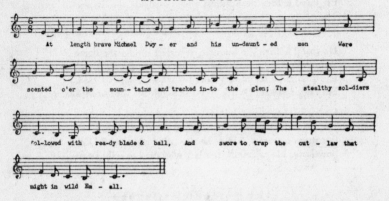

At length brave Michael Dwyer and his undaunted men
Were scented o'er the mountains and tracked into the glen;
The stealthy soldiers followed, with ready blade and ball,
And swore to trap the outlaw that night in wild Emall.

They prowled around the valley, and towards the dawn of day
Discovered where the faithful and fearless heroes lay.
Around the little cottage they formed in a ring,
And called out: 'Michael Dwyer! Surrender to the King!'

Thus answered Michael Dwyer—'Into this house we came
Unasked by those who own it; they cannot be to blame,
Then let those guiltless people, unquestioned, pass you through
And when they've passed in safety, I'll tell you what we'll do.'

Twas done. 'And now', said Dwyer, 'your dirty work begin;
You are a hundred outside—we're only four within;
We've heard your haughty summons, and this is our reply—
We're true United Irishmen, we'll fight until we die.'

Then burst the war's red lightning, then poured the leaden rain.
The hills around re-echoed the thunder-peals again;
The soldiers falling round him brave Dwyer sees with pride,
But, ah! one gallant comrade is wounded by his side.

Yet there are three remaining, good battle still to do;
Their hands are strong and steady, their aim is quick and true—
But hark that furious shouting the savage soldiers raise!
The house is fired around them! the roof is all ablaze

And brighter every moment the lurid flame arose.
And louder swelled the laughter and cheering of their foes;
Then spoke the brave McAllister, the weak and wounded man—
'You can escape, my comrades, and this shall be your plan:

'Place in my hands a musket, then lie upon the floor—
I'll stand before the soldiers and open wide the door;
They'll pour into my heart, boys, the fire of their array,
Then while their guns are empty, dash through them and away!'

He stood before the foemen, revealed amidst the flame;
From out their levelled pieces the wished-for volley came.
Up sprang the three survivors for whom the hero died,
But only Michael Dwyer burst through the ranks outside.

He baffled his pursuers, who followed like the wind.
He swam the river Slaney, and left them far behind,
But many a scarlet soldier he promised soon would fall
For those, his gallant comrades, who died in wild Emall.

T. D. Sullivan

THE WEXFORD MASSACRE
(1649)

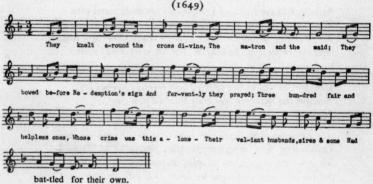

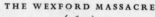

They knelt around the cross divine
The matron and the maid;
They bowed before Redemption's sign,
And fervently they prayed;
Three hundred fair and helpless ones,
Whose crime was this alone—
Their valiant husbands, sires and sons
Had battled for their own.

Had battled bravely, but in vain—
The Saxon won the fight;
The Irish corpses strewed the plain
Where Valour slept with Right.

And now that man of demon guilt
To fated Wexford flew—
The red blood reeking on his hilt,
Of hearts to Erin true.

He found them there—the young, the old,
The maiden, and the wife:
Their guardians brave in death were cold
Who dared for *them* the strife.
They prayed for mercy—God on high!
Before *Thy* cross they prayed,
And ruthless Cromwell bade them die
To glut the Saxon blade!

Three hundred fell—the stifled prayer
Was quenched in woman's blood;
Nor youth nor age could move to spare
From slaughter's crimson flood.
But nations keep a stern account
Of deeds that tyrants do;
And guiltless blood to Heaven will mount
And Heaven avenge it, too!

M. J. Barry

THE JACKETS GREEN

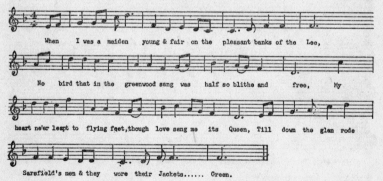

When I was a maiden young & fair on the pleasant banks of the Lee,
No bird that in the greenwood sang was half so blithe and free, My
heart ne'er leapt to flying feet, though love sang me its Queen, Till down the glen rode
Sarsfield's men & they wore their Jackets...... Green.

When I was a maiden young and fair on the pleasant banks of the Lee
No bird that in the greenwood sang was half so blithe and free,
My heart ne'er leapt to flying feet, though love sang me its Queen
Till down the glen rode Sarsfield's men, and they wore their Jackets Green.

Young Donal sat on his gallant grey like a king on a royal seat
And my heart leapt out on his regal way to worship at his feet;
O love had you come in those colours dressed and wooed with a soldier's
mien
I'd have laid my head on your throbbing breast for the sake of your Jacket
Green.

No hoarded wealth did my true love own save the good sword that he bore
But I loved him for himself alone and the colours that he wore,
For had he come in England's red to make me England's Queen
I'd have roved the high green hills instead for the sake of his Jacket Green.

When William stormed with shot and shell at the walls of Garryowen
In the breach of death my Donal fell and he sleeps near the Treaty Stone,
That breach the foeman never crossed while he swung his broadsword keen
But I do not weep my darling lost for he fell 'neath the Flag of Green.

When Sarsfield sailed away I wept as I heard the wild ochone,
I felt then dead as the men who slept 'neath the walls of Garryowen,
While Ireland held my Donal blest no wild seas rolled between,
I still could fold him to my breast all robed in his Jacket Green.

O Ireland, sad on thy lonely soul there breaks the winter sea,
But sadder and higher the wild waves roll from the hearts that break for
thee,
Yet grief shall come to thy heartless foes, and their thrones in the dust
be seen,
So Irish maids love none but those who wear the Jacket Green.

Michael Seanlan

THE WIND THAT SHAKES THE BARLEY

I sat within the valley green
I sat me with my true love;
My sad heart strove the two between,
The old love and the new love;
The old for her, the new that made
Me think of Ireland dearly,
While soft the wind blew down the glen
And shook the golden barley.

Twas hard the woeful words to frame
To break the ties that bound us;
But harder still to bear the shame
Of foreign chains around us.
And so I said, 'The mountain glen
I'll seek at morning early,
And join the brave United Men,'
While soft winds shook the barley.

While sad I kissed away her tears
My fond arms round her flinging,
The foeman's shot burst on our ears,
From out the wildwood ringing;
The bullet pierced my true love's side,
In life's young spring so early,
And on my breast in blood she died,
When soft winds shook the barley.

But blood for blood without remorse
I've taken at Oulart Hollow;
I've placed my true love's clay-cold corse
Where I full soon will follow;
And round her grave I wander drear,
Noon, night, and morning early,
With breaking heart whene'er I hear
The wind that shakes the barley!

Robert Dwyer Joyce

JAMES CONNOLLY

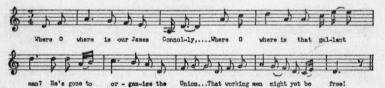

Where O where is our James Connolly
Where O where is that gallant man?
He's gone to organize the Union
That working men might yet be free!

Where O where is the Citizen Army
Where O where are those fighting men?
They've gone to join the Great Rebellion
And break the bonds of slavery.

And who'll be there to lead the van
O who'll be there to lead the van?
Who should be there but our James Connolly
The hero of each working man.

Who carries high that burning flag
Who carries high that burning flag?
Tis our James Connolly all pale and wounded
Who carries high our burning flag.

They carried him up to the jail
They carried him up to the jail
And there they shot him one bright May morning
And quickly laid him in his grave.

Who mourns now for our James Connolly
Who mourns for the fighting man?
O lay me down in yon green garden
And make my bearers Union men.

We laid him down in yon green garden
With Union men on every side
And swore we'd make one mighty Union
And fill that gallant man with pride.

Now all you noble Irishmen
Come join with me for liberty
And we will forge a mighty weapon
And smash the bonds of slavery!

DRUMBOE CASTLE

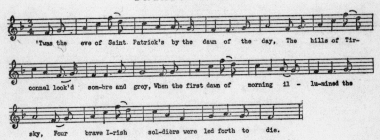

'Twas the eve of Saint Patrick's by the dawn of the day, The hills of Tirconnel look'd sombre and grey, When the first dawn of morning il - lu-mined the
sky, Four brave Irish sol-diers were led forth to die.

Twas the eve of St. Patrick's by the dawn of the day
The hills of Tirconnel looked sombre and grey
When the first dawn of morning illumined the sky
Four brave Irish soldiers were led forth to die.

They left their loved homes in a green Munster vale
And came to Tirconnel to fight for the Gael
Instead of true friends they met traitor and foe
Now uncoffined they lie in the woods of Drumboe.

The church bells rang loud in the cool morning air
To summon the faithful to penance and prayer
When a crash from the wild woods struck terror and woe
Twas the death knell of Daly shot dead at Drumboe.

Four Republican soldiers were dragged from their cells
Where for months they had suffered the torments of hell
No mercy they asked from their pitiless foe
And no mercy was shown by the thugs of Drumboe.

Let Triconnell no more boast of honour and fame,
All the waters of Finn could not wash out this shame
While the Finn and the Swilly continue to flow
This stain will remain on the thugs of Drumboe.

On 14th March, 1923, four Republican soldiers, Tim
O'Sullivan, Charles Daly, John Larkin and Dan Enright, were
executed at Drumboe, Co. Donegal.

BY MEMORY INSPIRED

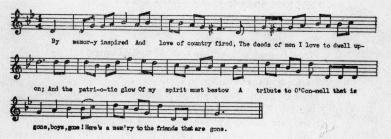

By Memory inspired
And love of country fired,
The deeds of Men I love to dwell upon;
And the patriotic glow
Of my spirit must bestow
A tribute to O'Connell that is gone, boys, gone!
Here's a memory to the friends that are gone.

In October Ninety-seven,
May his soul find rest in Heaven!
William Orr to execution was led on;
The jury, drunk, agreed
That Irish was his creed,
For perjury and threats drove them on, boys, on.
Here's the memory of John Mitchel that is gone!

In Ninety-eight, the month July,
The informer's pay was high,
When Reynolds gave the gallows brave McCann;
But McCann was Reynolds' first,
One could not allay his thirst,
So he brought up Bond and Byrne that are gone, boys, gone.
Here's the memory of the friends that are gone!

We saw a nation's tears
Shed for John and Henry Sheares,
Betrayed by Judas Captain Armstrong.
We may forgive, but yet
We never can forget
The poisoning of Maguire that is gone, boys, gone;
Our high star and true apostle that is gone!

How did Lord Edward die?
Like a man, without a sigh;
But he left his handiwork on Major Swan!
But Sirr, with steel-clad breast
And coward heart at best,
Left us cause to mourn Lord Edward that is gone, boys, gone.
Here's the memory of our friends that are gone!

September Eighteen-three
Closed this cruel history,
When Emmet's blood the scaffold flowed upon,
O had their spirits been wise
They might then realize
Their freedom—but we drink to Mitchel that is gone, boys,
                                                    gone.

Here's the memory of the friends that are gone!